CW01019609

The Entokil Man

The Entokil Man

The life of
Harold Maxwell-Lefroy

LAURENCE FLEMING

Dexter Haven
LONDON

Published in 2015 by Dexter Haven Publishing Ltd
Curtain House
134–146 Curtain Road
London
EC2A 3AR

ISBN 978-1-903660-17-1

A full CIP record for this book is available from the British Library

Typeset in Garamond by Dexter Haven Associates Ltd, London
Printed in India by Thomson Press, India

To
Cecil Anthony Maxwell-Lefroy
1907–1995

CONTENTS

LIST OF PLATES

EDITOR'S NOTE

The pound in 1900 was worth £104 of today's money, and in 1914 £97. If the reader will multiply by a hundred all the sums of money mentioned in the early part of the book he will get some idea of their value at that time. I am most grateful to Mr Robin Baillie for this information.

There were always 13 rupees to the pound, no matter how it fluctuated, and there were 16 annas to the rupee. A *lakh* of rupees was a hundred thousand, written as Rs. 1,00,000, and a hundred *lakhs* made a *crore*.

FOREWORD

My father joined the Burmah Oil Company in Rangoon in 1919, immediately on leaving the Army, having fought all through the First World War. In 1921 Burmah bought the Assam Oil Company as a subsidiary, and in 1934 my father moved to Digboi in Assam, as General Manager, where he remained until he retired in 1944.

Cecil Maxwell-Lefroy, the surviving son of Professor Harold Maxwell-Lefroy, joined Burmah in 1928 on leaving Cambridge. He worked only in Burma until being posted to Chittagong, in India, in 1938. During that time, and during the subsequent war, he came very often to Digboi and seems even to have worked there at some time. He would stay with my parents and they became great friends. He was to be General Manager of the Burmah Oil Company from 1954 to 1959.

His mother, who had been with him in Burma, used to spend the Hot Weather in the Windamere Hotel in Darjeeling, a hotel which has since achieved a certain international fame. My sister and I were at school in Darjeeling and, whenever our mother came to visit us – not too often as it was wartime – she would stay at the Windamere and we always had tea with Mrs Lefroy. We came to know her quite well. The two families coincided only once, at Bailey's Hotel in Gloucester Road in 1946. We went to the theatre together but I am sad to say that I cannot now remember what we went to see.

Many years later, in the course of writing a book, I found myself with questions about Burma that our widowed mother was unable to answer. She suggested that I write to Maxwell, as she called him, and I did so. A meeting followed, and then another, and I very soon realised that what he wanted more than anything was for someone to complete his father's biography. The research had been done, he said, but the researchers had failed to weld it into a book. In their own words, they had 'drowned in paper'.

So I undertook it. I submitted my drafts chapter by chapter, asking for comments, but no comments were made, neither were there any objections. The text he approved is the one reproduced here. He wanted it to be called *The Entokill Man*.

The research was in fact done, expertly and exhaustively, by Miss Helen Lefroy, the Professor's niece, and by her own nephew, Mr John Fullerton. Without them there would clearly have been no book and so this brings my grateful thanks to them for their monumental patience and perseverance. Their newspaper sources are all acknowledged and they have made excellent use of family memories, in particular those of Mr Cecil Maxwell-Lefroy.

Laurence Fleming
May 2015

CHAPTER I

At twenty-five past six on the evening of Wednesday the 14th of October 1925, Harold Maxwell-Lefroy, Professor of Entomology at the Imperial College of Science and Technology, and formerly Imperial Entomologist to the Government of India, died in St George's Hospital at Hyde Park Corner. He was forty-eight and had been unconscious for four days.

Earlier that year, on the 31st of March, the *Morning Post* had reported that the Professor had narrowly escaped death 'a few days ago' while experimenting in his laboratory.

> It seems that his investigations were concerned with the elimination of the fly danger, and he had reached a point where he had recorded in his notebook that the gases employed seemed too poisonous for use, when he himself was overcome. He was able to return to his private room, where he was found in a state of collapse.

From another source on the same day the Professor is reported as saying: 'I was so interested in the effect of the poison on the flies that I lost all account of time. Suddenly I felt difficulty in breathing, and it dawned on me my lungs were being filled with the gas.'

On that occasion he was able to warn two men working in an adjoining room before he became unconscious. To restore him, oxygen had to be administered for over an hour. 'The flies,' this report concludes, 'were found to be "very much alive" after the experiment.'

By the 2nd of April the *Morning Post* was able to inform its readers that the Professor was once again at work in his laboratory.

> 'I am able to get about again,' he said, 'but it will be some time before I am free of the infection of the lungs which the gas caused. I am surprised and sorry that the matter has received so much publicity, because such accidents are part of the normal daily risk of our work and we do not think very much about them.' Professor Maxwell-Lefroy had made a life study of insects, especially from the standpoint of their economic importance, and…as a result of his researches, the death watch beetle, which is threatening the historic buildings of England, can be eliminated at a fraction of the cost previously involved.

But this time the situation was more serious and not only the English papers were concerned. On the 13th of October the *Border Cities Star* of Windsor, Ontario, alerted its readers:

> Victim of His Own Science Is In Coma

> His lungs are filled with an unknown liquid which is slowly strangling him. The doctors say his symptoms indicate a gas containing chlorine. This is the second time that Prof. Lefroy has been a victim of his enthusiasm for science.

On the 15th, the death was reported in the *Border Cities Star*, *The Standard* of Buenos Aires, the Vancouver *Sun*, the *Cape Argus* of South Africa, the Toronto *Star*, the *New York Times*, the *Ceylon Observer* of Colombo and all the principal English papers. The *Westminster Gazette*, in the course of a long article, said:

> Professor Maxwell-Lefroy fell a martyr to his own ability. 'It is difficult to imagine a man more devoted to his work, and more helpful to those whose fortunate lot it had been to attend his lectures,' one of his students declared last night, before news of his death was known. 'If he had a fault it was that of too great reticence concerning his experiments, and many of us have remonstrated with him on the risks he took in the cause of science. He scoffed at the use of a gas mask, but neither of the misfortunes which befell him this year would have happened had he worn one.'

From Manchester the *Daily Sketch* said, among much else:

> In his early days Professor Lefroy was a schoolmaster, and later went to the West Indies and India, where he was the first official entomologist ever to be employed. In 1917 he went to Mesopotamia to do furious battle with the sandfly, and was described by the *Daily Sketch* as 'The Pied Piper of the War.' Temperamentally he was of a retiring disposition, but conspicuously sincere in everything he undertook.

At the end of its article, the *Daily News* noted;

> Professor Lefroy was hon. curator of the Insect House at the Zoo, and had been entomologist to the Imperial Department of Agriculture for the West Indies, Imperial Entomologist for India and Imperial Silk Specialist for India. He was educated at Marlborough and Cambridge, and during the war served as a lieutenant-colonel with the Mesopotamian Expeditionary Force.

Under the heading 'Tragedy and Science' the *Daily Graphic* wrote: 'The death of Professor Lefroy is marked by almost every element of great tragedy. The distinguished scientist has sacrificed his own life to his own secret. The formula of the gas with which he was experimenting…was known to him alone…'

The *Daily Mirror*:

> Probably no man realised so fully the menace to man of the insect world and no one has done more to fight it. 'Intellectual man must win against blind insects,' he said. Professor Lefroy was the fourth son of Mr. C.J. Maxwell-Lefroy, of Itchel Manor, Crondall, Hants, and he married Kathleen Hamilton, daughter of Mr William O'Meara, of British Guiana, in 1904. It was his wife who, alarmed at his long absence from home, hurried to the laboratory and found him unconscious on the floor.

The *Daily Herald* and the *Morning Advertiser* carried notices of the event, as did *The Times* and *Morning Post*.

The *Morning Post*:

> 'I want,' he said, 'before I die to see the death watch beetle exterminated. My own researches and those of my staff have made its destruction an easy matter. The cost is infinitely less than when Westminster was threatened, and my own laboratory has not benefited or wished to

benefit by a penny. We have given our advice; we have provided the services of the clerical staff free, but we have had printed a card which we enclose to enquirers, asking them if they find the advice valuable to make a donation to the London Hospital.' The Professor was an extensive writer. Among his best-known publications are: 'Indian Insect Pests' (1906), 'Indian Insect Life' (1910) and a 'Manual of Entomology' (1923). He made many contributions to the *West Indian Bulletin* and the *Agricultural Journal of India*, and was the author of 'Memoirs of the Agricultural Department of India'.

The Times:

He believed that it was often possible to encourage the natural insect enemies of insects, and some of this most interesting work was the result of observation in the field of what species of insects preyed on others and how these benefactors could be transferred to areas where their services were required. An old friend writes: 'Lefroy was eager and high-strung, impatient of every obstacle that seemed to stand in his way, and disposed to optimism as to the line he was pursuing at any moment. His surcharge of energy and unflagging confidence often put him out of sympathy with slower or more cautious minds and led him into not a few animated controversies. But while his opponents were still laboriously proving him to be wrong Lefroy had already discovered his own mistakes and, profiting by them, was hot on a new scent. Continued resentment was foreign to his disposition, but in any case he was far too busy with the work of the moment to have time for it. He was generous and unselfish, delightful as a friend, and ready to sacrifice everything except his work and his friends.' He was an ardent and dangerous motorist. It was an experience to be driven by him in a car whose battered wings gave little confidence, as fast as the car could go, through London traffic, in company with a biscuit-box of noxious living insects, a few glass-bottles of poisons, and a cylinder of some lethal gas. In revenge for such a trip I once took him from Regent's Park to St Paul's and back in a very fast car with quick acceleration, intending to 'show off' a little. Lefroy took not the slightest notice of the risks, but continued to describe a new method of cooking the goose of the red boll weevil, drawing diagrams on the back of an envelope and thrusting them on the driver's attention. Lefroy was not only a great investigator but a wholly delightful personality. He was married and has left one son.

A post-mortem was conducted at St George's Hospital on the 15th of October, shortly after midday, and an inquest was held by the Westminster Coroner on the 16th. The Professor's death was reported in the *Times of India*, Bombay, the *Bombay Chronicle*, the Baltimore *Sun* and the *Egyptian Gazette* of Alexandria.

In the wider world, a Peace Pact was initialled at the Swiss health resort of Locarno, by which Germany, Belgium, France, Great Britain and Italy mutually agreed the peace of Western Europe.

On the 17th, there were further reports of his death, in the *Daily Chronicle* of Georgetown, British Guiana, in the *Ceylon Observer* of Colombo, the *Standard* of Kingston, Canada, and the *Christian Patriot* of Madras, international recognition of an international name, whose work had been of international importance.

He was buried on that day, a Saturday, in Kensal Green Cemetery, London W10. The Chief Mourner was the Professor's surviving son, Cecil Maxwell-Lefroy, who had just gone up to Cambridge. In his words:

My mother was overcome by shock and the funeral arrangements were made by his Cambridge friend and contemporary, Arthur M. Cohen. It was literally the first day of full term. My tutor had heard about it and he summoned me and said, 'Well, don't bother about *exeats* or anything' and we went down and went to Kensal Green. There was quite a small gathering there. It wasn't a big thing at all. I was rather surprised as Father was so well-known. Among the mourners was a gentleman in a red beard whom I did not recognise. He came over and said, 'I am your Uncle Jack.' I had never seen him before. He was my father's elder brother. He had quarrelled with my father and they had been estranged for some years. It can be said that most Lefroys have a quarrelsome or contentious streak that was totally lacking in my father unless he was unjustly provoked. My mother said he had refused to let Father be buried alongside the other members of the family in the churchyard of Crondall Village, but I find this difficult to believe. Strangely, Mother would never visit Father's grave, although for many years she paid a man to look after it.

Among other mourners, reported in both *The Times* and the *Morning Post*, were two cousins and a sister-in-law and her husband. Imperial College was represented by its Rector, the Professor of Zoology and five other professors. The Director of the Natural History Museum was there, the director of East Malling Research Station was represented and there were two representatives from the Museum of Zoology in Cambridge.

'There was also present,' stated the *Morning Post*, 'a body of the late Professor's former students and Professor Awati, of Bombay, one of the Professor's former students.'

The results of the inquest were reported in the *Madras Mail* and the Colombo *Daily News* on the 19th of October and in the Calcutta *Amrita Bazar Patrika* on the 22nd. *The Times* produced a special supplement on Tobacco on the 20th, in which there were two articles by Harold Maxwell-Lefroy, 'Nicotine as an Insecticide' and 'Tobacco Pests'.

The *Gardeners' Chronicle* carried a long obituary notice on the 24th of October and, a week later, the magazine *Nature* had this to say:

> One who had the pleasure of working with him during his earliest days at South Kensington will never forget the cheerful optimism with which he undertook the most herculean labour, the extraordinary speed with which he worked, the zest with which he attacked and demolished every new obstacle, and the unexpectedness of many of his actions ... His death at the early age of forty-eight leaves entomology the poorer by the loss of a very remarkable man.

The Annual Report of Council at King's College, Cambridge, of the 14th of November, included this sentence: 'During his nine years in India he revolutionized previous methods of studying the insect pests of agricultural crops, he carried out personally and superintended an amazing amount of research into the life histories of many serious pests, and devised practical remedies.'

An obituary notice in the *Annals of Applied Biology* of November 1925, under the signature of A.D. Imms, enlarges on this subject:

...in 1903 he obtained the important position of Imperial Entomologist to the Department of Agriculture for India. It was in this capacity that Lefroy had his full opportunity of exercising his undoubted abilities for organization and for dealing with big practical problems. At the Pusa Institute he succeeded in building up a most efficient department and staffed it with men trained under his own supervision... There is no doubt that India owes much to Lefroy's pioneer influence, since he not only laid the foundations of much valuable economic work, but he also gave his subject definite status in the eyes of the Government, and he convinced officials over him of the vast toll insects were exacting in the reduction of the yield of the staple crops of the country.

The Entomologist, *The Entomologist's Monthly Magazine* and the *Entomological News* all carried obituaries or appreciations in November, and in December An Appreciation from Sir Frank Baines, CBE, MVO, Director of Works, HM Office of Works, appeared in the *Journal of the Royal Institute of British Architects*, principally in connection with the role the Professor had played in the restoration of the roof of Westminster Hall.

There was an article in *The Phoenix* in December, under the initials J.D.

In 1923 he published a Manual of Entomology which was written with the assistance of some of his students. If it were not for his sad death perhaps he would have given us a book dealing with the broad conception of economic entomology, based on his wide experience and association with big entomological problems, which would have brought the importance of development of the applied aspect of the subject before a wider public.

The *Journal of Economic Entomology* and the *Journal of the Bombay Natural History Society* published their tributes in December and early in the next year *Tropical Agriculture*, the official journal of the Imperial College of Tropical Agriculture in Trinidad, did so too. It was given pride of place in the journal, surrounded by a deep black border.

While in the West Indies he studied the insect pests of the principal crops, publishing an excellent account of the Moth Borer of the sugar-cane, and papers on the Scale Insects of the West Indies. While in India in addition to his studies of pests of crops and the development of methods of control of such pests, he gave much attention to the improvement of production of lac and silk...

But perhaps most surprising of all, an unidentified cutting remains, tantalisingly incomplete.

SECRETS OF NATURE

Professor Maxwell Lefroy's Memorable Work in Filming Insect Life. The British film industry has suffered a very great loss by the death of Professor Maxwell Lefroy, because in his crowded hour of life he found time to present on the screen, in the wonderful 'Secrets of Nature' series, some of his most fascinating studies of insect life. In that respect he was a notable example.

Six months later, on Thursday the 22nd of April 1926, the *Morning Post*, under the heading 'Lost Laboratory Secrets', published an article on 'Professor Lefroy's unfinished work'.

Yesterday, Professor Balfour Browne, the distinguished entomologist of Cambridge University, who has recently succeeded to the post held by Professor Lefroy at the Imperial College of Science, gave a *Morning Post* representative an account of some of the difficulties he had had to contend with in regard to the disposal of material and apparatus found in the laboratory used by the dead scientist.

Buried for Safety

'The task of those whose duty it was to search the laboratory was a very dangerous one,' he said. 'It must be remembered that no one knew exactly what Lefroy, who was undoubtedly one of the most brilliant men of his day, was doing at the time of his death. There is no doubt at all, however, that he had been mixing all sorts of substances together and many bottles and other receptacles containing various dangerous chemicals were found in the laboratory... Many of the articles found were buried for safety's sake.' Professor Balfour Browne added that there was no one in England able to take Lefroy's place as regards the applied entomological work he was carrying out... His activities covered a wide range, and during the war he saved Australia vast sums of money by devising a means while visiting that country of destroying a pest which was threatening the wheat crop and had already caused very serious damage. His ambition was by his own efforts and those of his pupils to organise an army of fighting entomologists, men who had been trained to study the habits of pests and who would be capable of applying the knowledge obtained to each economic problem as it arose.

Although he did not live to achieve this ambition, the army of fighting entomologists was to appear, with many of its weapons forged, and its tactics suggested, by Professor Maxwell-Lefroy.

CHAPTER II

Over the last two centuries, Lefroys have established themselves in Ireland, England, Australia and Canada, but they all descend from Antoine l'Offroy, a Protestant fugitive from Cambrai, who arrived in Canterbury, with his wife and son, about 1586.

Cambrai is situated in one of the most desirable, and most disputed, areas of northern Europe. A part of France since 1678, it was previously in the Spanish Netherlands and before that in the territories of the Duke of Burgundy. Originally, however, from the fifth century, it was an independent bishopric, Cambrésis, and its inhabitants were appropriately strong-minded and independent, owing their allegiance only to their own bishop and, through him, to God.

Its prosperity was based on weaving, fine wool and very fine linen. It gave its name to 'cambric'; 'batiste' is also said to have originated there, on the loom of a weaver called Baptiste. These were the finest materials available – other than silk and before the advent of cotton – and they were used throughout Europe for undergarments and, in particular, shrouds, during the Middle Ages. There was a constant trade with England, a source of both the wool and the flax.

In the 1560s, when we may suppose Antoine l'Offroy to have been born, the Spanish Netherlands were in a state of turmoil, as the teachings of Luther and Calvin spread through them. The Duke of Alva, a Spanish general, conducted a ruthless persecution of the Protestant forces and their leaders between 1568 and 1573, but he could not destroy their Protestantism. In 1579 the Union of Utrecht joined the seven northern Protestant provinces.

Their leader was William the Silent, determined to achieve complete independence from Spain; but he was opposed by the Duke of Parma, the Spanish Governor-General, equally determined to bring the whole area once more under Spanish domination. Hainault and Artois, which flanked Cambrai, sided with him and he embarked initially on the reconquest of the southern provinces. He completed this in 1585 when, on the 15th of August, Antwerp surrendered, after a long and debilitating siege.

It was presumably then that the Protestant Antoine l'Offroy, facing a life of constant persecution and arbitrary fiscal penalties, decided to leave. His alternatives were to go north to the seven provinces, still in a state of unrest, or to go west, to the comparative calm of Protestant England. He decided on the latter and joined a well-established community of French-speaking Huguenots – known to the locals as 'strangers' – in Canterbury. He became an important member of that community.

He travelled with his wife, Marie de Hornes, or Hoorn, and an infant son. He seems to have been a landowner rather than a rich merchant, as he brought with him a coat-of-arms as well as a large sum of money and many jewels. The coat-of-arms, silver diamond-shaped trellis on a green ground, was not confirmed until 1857, by the Ulster King at Arms, but the design is much older than that. It carries with it the motto *Mutare sperno*, 'I scorn to change', formidable and even dangerous, since it can so easily deviate into 'I do not compromise' or 'I am always right'.

The family prospered from the beginning. By the middle of the seventeenth century it was involved in the silk-dyeing industry at Canterbury and, in 1702, Thomas Lefroy, Antoine's great-great-grandson, was able to marry into the English gentry. His bride was

Phoebe Thomson, of Petham near Canterbury, and it was their son, Anthony Lefroy, who founded the Lefroy families as we know them.

He was a banker, of Leghorn, or Livorno, in northern Italy, a city with a long history of international trade, free both as port and city, neutral since 1691. He served an apprenticeship in a merchant's house in London and then went to Leghorn to join the banking house of Peter Langlois. Here, in 1738, he married the daughter of that house, Elizabeth.

Of the two sons who survived infancy the elder, Anthony Peter, went into the Army. Almost all his service was spent in Ireland and he married an Irish lady, Ann Gardner. They retired to Limerick, where he is buried. His descendants are known as the Irish Lefroys.

The younger son, Isaac Peter George, was ordained priest in the Church of England in 1772, having received his BA from Christ Church, Oxford, in 1767. He became MA and a Fellow of All Souls in 1772.

He was 'presented to' the Rectory of Compton in Surrey in 1777, that is to say, it was purchased for him, possibly by his future mother-in-law, Mrs Brydges; and in 1778 he was presented to the Vicarage of Ashe, in Hampshire, by his uncle Benjamin Langlois, the purchase to cover three generations. In that year he married Anne Brydges and they moved into the modernised parsonage at Ashe, a neighbouring parish to Steventon, where the Reverend George Austen was Rector.

Anne Brydges had two sisters and two brothers.

Charlotte married a Mr Harrison as her second husband and Jane Austen was to write of her, in 1813: 'She is a sweet woman, still quite a sweet woman in herself, & so like her sister! I could almost have thought I was speaking to Mrs. Lefroy.'

Deborah married Henry Maxwell, a sugar magnate from Barbados, where he had been in partnership with the Lascelles of Harewood. They lived at Ewshott House, near Crondall in Hampshire and at Ramsbury, in Wiltshire. Their London house was in Harley Street and there, in 1789, Deborah burned to death 'while her attention was engaged in writing' – invitations to dinner. A candle had ignited her muslin dress.

Of her two brothers the younger, Samuel Egerton Brydges, is the more interesting. Convinced himself that they were heirs, through a great-grandmother, to the barony of Chandos, he persuaded his elder brother to put it to the test. The case was heard and they lost it. Not until 1814 was he able to purchase a baronetcy for himself.

They were the children of Edward Brydges, of Wotton Court in Kent, and his wife Jemima, daughter of Dr William Egerton, Prebendary of Canterbury and Chancellor of Hereford. It is fair to assume that Anne brought with her a substantial dowry.

Anne Lefroy was a few years older than Jane Austen, but it is clear that they were great friends. 'My black cap was openly admired by Mrs. Lefroy, and secretly I imagine everyone else in the room.' The Tom Lefroy who seems to have fallen a little in love with Miss Austen was Thomas Langlois Lefroy of the Irish family, on a visit to his uncle at Ashe. She does not appear to have returned his affection and he went back to Ireland, where he was called to the Bar and later became Lord Chief Justice.

Anne Lefroy fell from her horse and was killed on the 16th of December 1804, Jane Austen's twenty-ninth birthday. The event distressed her deeply. Four years later she wrote, as part of a longer poem:

I see her here with all her smiles benign,
    Her looks of eager love, her accents sweet,
That voice and countenance almost divine,
    Expression, harmony, alike complete.

The Reverend George survived his wife by little more than a year, having been, in the words of Sir Egerton Brydges, 'an excellent man, of courtly manners, who knew the world and had mixed in it'.

Their son, John Henry George, succeeded to the livings of Compton and Ashe, but on the death of his mother's brother-in-law,

Henry Maxwell, in 1818, he inherited the estate of Ewshott House. He died in 1823, leaving a family of six sons and five daughters. His younger brother, Benjamin, who had married a niece of Jane Austen, followed him as Rector of Ashe.

Ewshott House, afterwards known as Itchel Manor, was a handsome, brick-built house from the late seventeenth century, at some distance from the village of Crondall. It had seven bays, corner pavilions of two bays and overhanging eaves. Sash windows and a porch were added in the middle of the eighteenth century and the dormer windows were enlarged early in the nineteenth. It stood in several thousand acres of the richest farmland, producing an income to keep one family in great comfort, to dower the daughters into respectable marriages and to assist the younger sons into the Army, the Navy, the Church or the Law. It had considerable pleasure grounds and two enormous walled gardens.

Itchel Manor was mentioned under that name in the Domesday Book, when it was the property of the Bishop of Winchester. A house on that site was burnt down in 1680 and a new one built in the same place by Squire Bathurst. He seems to have been a disagreeable and miserly individual, traditionally murdered by his Italian valet while gloating over his money. Traditionally, too, his body was walled up somewhere in the building and it is a fact that, when the house was demolished in 1954, a portrait of the Squire was found behind panelling in one of the bedrooms; but there was no sign of a skeleton. The Squire, however, was considered to be responsible for the bumping and thumping which occurred from time to time behind various walls in the house.

A phantom carriage and horses also drew up at the front door, heard rather than seen. It was reputed to be the carriage of a previous owner, Nicholas Linwood, a director of the East India Company who, with his postilion, was shot dead by highwaymen on Bagshot Heath. The horses thereupon bolted, only coming to a halt outside the front door of the Manor.

Many members of the Lefroy family, their staff and their guests, are known to have heard the arrival of this coach. Indeed the only sister of Harold Maxwell-Lefroy, when helping to dress her mother for a party, once remarked that their first guests were already arriving.

'Oh no,' her mother replied. 'The ghost always comes early.'

Mysterious footsteps were heard and a 'grey lady', thought to be Mrs Maxwell herself, was also reported. A certain Captain Fraser, visiting the house in 1840, documented all these phenomena. There was the sound of a heavily laden carriage passing under the window of a particular bedroom. There was talk of a flock of sheep arriving very late on a winter's night, curiously leaving no hoofmarks and doing no damage.

The haunted part of the house was rebuilt, as were the stables, but the mysterious sounds, which always began at about eleven o'clock at night, continued. They continued, too, after the bailiff's house, at one time thought to be the source of all the trouble, was demolished. Footsteps, in particular, were heard on different occasions by both the parents of Harold Maxwell-Lefroy. Under all the circumstances, it is not surprising that they had difficulty keeping servants.

Charles Edward, eldest son of the Reverend John Henry George, was called to the Bar at Lincoln's Inn in 1836. With his brother Anthony he accidentally discovered the Crondall Hoard of seventh-century gold coins while on a shooting expedition. These are now in the Ashmolean Museum. He was Secretary to the Speaker of the House of Commons from 1840 to 1856.

In 1845 he married Janet, daughter and heiress of James Walker, LLD, FRS, a rich and distinguished Scottish engineer who numbered the harbours at Belfast and Dover among his achievements. Shortly after the Crimean War, Charles Edward sold to the nation the enormous area of land on which the military establishments at Aldershot and Farnborough now stand. The price was £30,000, to be paid in gold; but this money, strangely enough, has never been found. Charles Edward died in 1861, leaving two sons.

In 1872, Charles James Maxwell, the elder of these, who had inherited the Itchel property, married Elizabeth Catherine, the eldest daughter of Alfred Henry McClintock, MD, LLD, an eminent surgeon of Dublin, later to become President of the College of Surgeons. His first cousin, raised to the peerage as Baron Rathdonnell in 1868, was married to an aunt of Charles James, Anne Lefroy.

Elizabeth Catherine was extremely good-looking, masterful, fiercely Protestant and socially very ambitious. Her family came originally from Dundalk, in Co. Louth. She had an expensive taste in clothes and was fond of giving large parties. Her husband was an easy-going country gentleman, magistrate and patron of the living, a keen huntsman and shot. He was also very fond of social life and there is a suggestion that he enjoyed bestowing handsome presents, particularly on his women friends. Between them they consumed the bulk of the Lefroy fortune and by 1900 were obliged to move into a smaller house on the estate.

In 1875, after the fashion of the time, Maxwell and Lefroy were legally hyphenated together, a thing under contemplation ever since the Lefroys had inherited the Maxwell property. It only remained to produce a family of brilliant, successful sons, who would marry well and rise to the top of their professions, and brilliant, beautiful daughters, who would all marry into the peerage. Of excellent constitution, Elizabeth Catherine gave birth to five sons and a daughter within ten years of her marriage, and another son six years later.

Her children, however, were to disappoint her.

The eldest son, Charles Alfred Henry, born in 1872, was epileptic. He was shipped off to Tasmania, where his great-uncle, Sir John Henry Lefroy, had been Governor in 1880, in the care of a keeper. He died in 1953, supported for eighty years by the family.

The second son, George Langlois, born in 1874, was given some training as a farmer and then exported to Canada. On returning home, he was found to have acquired a colonial accent and was sent straight back again by his outraged mother. He married a lady from Bridge

Creek, Manitoba, and spent the rest of his life farming there. He had one daughter and died in 1941.

Cecil, the third son, known as Jack, was born in 1876. Very brilliant mathematically, he went into the Navy, won many prizes at Osborne and obtained five Firsts in the promotion examination for Lieutenant. He became a specialist in long-range gunnery and achieved the rank of Commander before he was thirty. He became Captain in 1912. His war service took him to the Indian Ocean, the Dardanelles – where he was commended for service in action – and to Scapa Flow, where he commanded HMS *Blake*. In 1919 he was awarded the CMG – the Most Distinguished Order of St Michael and St George – but in 1922 he was retired, under the so-called Geddes Axe. In the words of one of his daughters, he was 'a difficult man so never had a happy ship'. He married in 1913, a pretty girl from a rich Lancashire cotton family, just acceptable to his mother. They had a son and four daughters and he died in 1931.

It was Jack who inherited the Itchel Manor estate on his father's death in 1908. The house was already so heavily mortgaged that he was unable to live in it himself. It was let continuously and the land leased to tenant farmers.

Harold, the fourth son, was born in 1877. Quite as brilliant, in a different way, as his brother Jack, he chose to become an entomologist, a hitherto unknown, and highly unfashionable, species of scientist, and to marry, from his mother's point of view, most unsuitably.

Evelyn, born in 1879, and always known as Dolly, was Harold's favourite brother. He became a mining engineer and went out to India. He married quietly in 1906, fathered a son and two daughters and died in 1962.

Kathleen Margaret, the only daughter, was born in 1882. In spite of being as beautiful as her mother, she failed to marry into the peerage. Her husband, Colonel Philip Lewis, by whom she had five sons, was a distinguished officer in the Royal Artillery, being awarded both the CMG and the DSO. She died in 1979.

Patrick Egerton, the sixth son, was not born until 1888. He too went into the Navy and was killed 'by a stray bullet' in action at the Dardanelles in 1915.

These children received the standard upper-class upbringing, well provided for but almost devoid of affection. Their time would have been spent largely in the company of nursemaids, housemaids, grooms and gardeners, contact with their parents being rare and formal. They lived in an independent nursery world, with its own codes, secrets and feuds, some of which were to last for a long time.

And the house in which they lived was reputed to be haunted.

CHAPTER III

The fragmentation of the family, which makes the reconstruction of their childhood years so difficult, began early.

Jack and Patrick both went to Osborne, but at completely different times as there were twelve years between them. The other boys all went to separate schools, although they all began at Church Hill House, a large, rather ugly late-nineteenth-century building in the village of Crondall, then being run as a preparatory school.

Its advertisement in *The Times*, in 1891, ran as follows:

EDUCATION – Church Hill, Crondall, Farnham. Invigorating country life. Healthiest in England (see Registered Report). Successful preparation for public schools and Navy. French and German guaranteed, cricket fields and football fields, tennis, carpenters' shop, school farm, riding ponies. Large addition to premises. Address 'Principal'.

The Principal was a Mr Alexander Somerville Bassett Scott, a scion of the Buccleuch family. Carpentry was taught in a shed behind the gymnasium, which was also used for concerts. The school kept its own ponies and a rough-riding sergeant instructor came over every week from Aldershot. The intention would have been to produce tough, self-reliant boys, able to think for themselves in an emergency, but not necessarily able to think things out.

The words 'invigorating' and 'healthiest', as used in this advertisement, certainly meant cold baths, open windows and unheated dormitories, classrooms and corridors. As an avowed purpose of education at that time was, in the words of the Reverend William Keble Martin, to train boys 'to fill a small place in that great beneficent and Christian institution, the British Empire', much of which lay within the tropics, this insistence on imperviousness to cold must seem to be somewhat misplaced. It was heat that caused so much misery to Empire builders.

The Maxwell-Lefroys, however, were day boys and were probably spared many of the routine discomforts. One of their contemporaries, a boarder, was Claude Grahame-White, later to become celebrated as air ace and pioneer aviator; and it is thought that it was through this connection that Harold and Dolly were sent off to school in Germany. The reason for this is not known. Schools in Germany were no cheaper than they were in England; they were perhaps a little stricter. Possibly their parents felt that Harold, in particular, a wayward boy, was in need of more disciplined control.

The daughter of Harold's second-eldest brother, Langlois, wrote, in 1980: 'About Uncle Harold. Many times my father mentioned him. He said Harold was never interested in the sports, mischief, etc. that the other boys indulged in, but was more often to be found on his stomach looking into a puddle with a magnifying glass, studying the bugs.'

This alone would have been enough to alarm almost any parent of the time. Harold acquired enough German to win the Dutton Prize at Marlborough in 1892 as a result of this excursion, but it must have weakened any feeling he and Dolly might previously have had of being members of a family. On their return to England in 1890, Harold was sent to Marlborough, while Dolly followed Rudyard Kipling to the United Services College at Westward Ho!

Their father had been at Eton and was later commissioned into the XIVth Hussars. The four younger sons of one of the Irish Lefroys, the Very Reverend Jeffry, had been to Marlborough. It was cheaper than Eton but neither very near Crondall, nor very far away from it. Westward Ho! was cheaper still, and even further away.

Whatever the reasons for it, Marlborough was by no means an untoward choice. If Harold's interest in insects was not actively encouraged, it was certainly not actively discouraged. The College stands at the west end of the town of Marlborough within reach, for a reasonably energetic boy, of Savernake Forest, the River Kennet and the Marlborough Downs, sources of rich and varied insect life.

Harold entered Preshute House, a house some way from the College, under the housemastership of Mr W.E. Mullins, who had been there since 1872 and now ran the house with the aid of his daughters. From this we may perhaps assume that the running of the house was largely left to the prefects, possibly accounting for the great dislike of all authority shown by Harold later in his life.

His career at Marlborough seems not to have been particularly glorious, in terms of the public school ethic of those days. We know that he was not on any school side in sports, that he did not represent his house in any game, or in swimming or the Rifle Corps. We know that he was in the Engineering Class, which catered mainly for those trying to enter the Army, and won their Science Prize in 1894. He became a House Prefect. But – what is perhaps more surprising than any of these things – we also know that he was not a member of the Natural History Society.

This had been founded in 1864, by the Reverend T.A. Preston, and was an extremely flourishing affair. In Harold's last term, it is estimated that it had some two hundred members. It was the particular concern of the Classics master, Edward Meyrick, at that time in his middle thirties, who was its President. He had already spent some years in Australia and New Zealand and was later to become a Fellow of the Royal Society, largely on account of his work on the Australian *lepidoptera*, butterflies and moths.

Three contemporaries of Harold's, all members of the Society, were: Arthur Hill, later to be distinguished as a botanist, to be knighted and become Director of the Royal Botanic Gardens at Kew; William Keble Martin, who was to become a parish priest and to publish, in 1965, his life's work, *The Concise British Flora in Colour*; and L.C.H. Young, who was to re-organise, re-set and re-catalogue the Butterfly Collection of the Bombay Natural History Society.

They were all, however, in different houses and there is no reason to suppose that they knew one another. Certainly Harold does not appear to have kept in touch with any of them after leaving school. What is more remarkable is that Harold's housemaster did not insist on his joining the Natural History Society as a younger and more forceful man might well have done. We may suppose that he was left in comparative peace to pursue his interest in his own time, without any unwanted guidance from the Society's President – who was interested principally in butterflies and moths – or from anyone else.

Harold left Marlborough at the end of the Summer Term in 1895, having obtained entrance, with Arthur Hill, to King's College, Cambridge.

At the final house supper he was obliged to make a speech on the subject of 'Games' and it would be most interesting to know what he actually said since, in the words of his son, 'he took no interest in any kind of ball-game.'

The most frequent performer at the event was A.W.F. Blunt, who had also been at Church Hill House in Crondall. He was later to become Bishop of Bradford and to precipitate, quite unwittingly, the Abdication Crisis of 1936; he was also the father of Anthony Blunt. On this occasion he seems to have proposed the health of 'The Visitors', to have sung, with chorus, a plantation song, 'De Ringtailed Coon', and to have participated in a quartet, 'Students' Parting Song'.

Harold replied to a fellow prefect's speech, 'Leaving Fellows', his speech following a rendering of 'Mandalay' by another fellow prefect. One of his prizes is still recorded on the boards at Preshute House.

Entomology, the study of insects, was not a subject for separate study at Cambridge at that time. Although the English word is dated in the Oxford English Dictionary at 1766, taken directly from the French *entomologie* which, in its turn, derives from the Greek work *entomon*, an insect, as a scientific study it aroused very little interest until the second half of the nineteenth century and textbooks were few and far between.

A Manual of British Coleoptera by J.F. Stephens had been published without illustrations in 1839. This was a book about beetles. J.O. Westwood had written *An Introduction to Modern Classification of Insects*, and had contributed notes to the translated version of *A Treatise on Insects Injurious to Gardens*, published by V. Kollar in 1840. But, in 1852, a very remarkable Englishwoman, Eleanor Ormerod, began, at the age of twenty-four, what would now be regarded as her amateur studies.

She was the youngest of the ten children of George Ormerod, FRS, owner of a large estate at Sedgbury Park in Gloucestershire. She dissected beetles herself, and no doubt observed closely any other insects which lived on the estate. She became an acknowledged authority and, in 1868, assisted the Royal Horticultural Society to form a collection of insect pests, both on the farm and in the garden. For this she was awarded the Society's Flora Medal.

In 1877 she published a seven-page pamphlet, *Notes for the Observations of Injurious Insects*, and continued to publish her *Annual Reports on Injurious Insects and Farm Pests* until 1898. In 1881 she published *A Manual of Injurious Insects with Methods of Prevention and Remedy* and in the following year she became Consulting Entomologist to the Royal Agricultural Society. She lectured regularly at the Royal Agricultural College, Cirencester. A second, enlarged, edition of her *Manual of Injurious Insects* was published in 1890 and this, and all her previous publications, must have been known to Harold at Cambridge, if not at Marlborough.

It is interesting to note that one of the references she gave in 1877 was the Reverend T.A. Preston, founder of the Marlborough Natural History Society.

In her published lectures at the Institute of Agriculture in 1883, Miss Ormerod said:

> It is important to know that the manner of insect life is fixed according to regular laws... But once get the real history fixed as a fact, and then we know how to act.

> We should in all cases look at the special habit of the pest.

Of a particular beetle she said:

> Both as weevils and grubs they feed on Aphides of various kinds, and are of such great service in keeping down the Hop Aphis that they should not ever be destroyed.

Other comments were:

> Thus by studying the points of some one kind of attack, we see for ourselves that all other attacks which have the same points may be lessened by the same kind of treatment.

> Clearing all weeds that attract the Moths is one method of preventing increase.

It was pioneer work, for which Miss Ormerod became the first woman to receive an honorary degree from Edinburgh University, in 1900.

Harold's acquaintance with Miss Ormerod's work can only be assumed, but there were two men then at Cambridge with whom he undoubtedly came in contact and whose influence on him can scarcely be exaggerated. David Sharp (1840–1922) was the Curator of Insects in the University Museum of Zoology, and Adam Sedgwick (1854–1913) was the Reader in Animal Embryology, later to become Professor of Zoology.

David Sharp qualified as a doctor and for many years was in sole charge of a wealthy patient in Scotland, during which time he was able to devote almost his whole attention to entomology. His obituary notice, from the Royal Society, informs us that, by the age of twenty-three, he had a collection of 662 named species of British beetle. His first publications, however, were about foreign ones, the

Staphylinidae, or rove-beetles, those of Japan in 1874 and of the Amazon in 1876.

On the death of his patient in 1883, he moved to Southampton and two years later became Editor of the Insect Section of the *Zoological Record*, taking over the whole publication in 1891. In 1888 he moved to Cambridge, where he remained as Curator of Insects until he retired in 1909.

He seems to have been 'a delightful companion, with an inexhaustible fund of dry humour under all circumstances'. He was 'most liberal in giving his assistance and encouragement' to younger men, and those with less experience than himself. While he did not specifically write about economic entomology, that is to say the study of the effect of insect life upon the economy, he must have thought about it a great deal. His obituary notice quotes him as having written, in 1903:

> I have given much attention to Economic Entomology during the last twenty years, and of late specially. I am convinced that the internal parasites are the things that keep the balance of nature in the insect world fairly true. The predators are of value, but it is the internal parasites that are the great agents. They *are not seen*, and consequently we totally undervalue them, but I believe all insects may be kept down by the aid of well selected parasites.

Adam Sedgwick had also been educated at Marlborough, and then at Trinity College, Cambridge. He had visited South Africa, had published papers about his visit between 1884 and 1888, and was the author of a standard textbook on zoology.

He waited for twenty-five years to become Professor of Zoology, but in the meanwhile he built up a magnificently equipped laboratory which he filled with eager and enthusiastic pupils. He approached the teaching of biology and embryology in a way never attempted before and was later entirely to re-organise the Zoology School. His pupils were to find their way to all parts of the globe, as professors and as research workers.

It was therefore at this point in his life that Harold was able to rationalise his interest in insects, and what appears to have been an instinctive understanding of them. He had absorbed most of the available wisdom on the subject and was no longer simply regarded as an eccentric, as he must have been both at Marlborough and at home. He obtained First Class Honours in the Natural Sciences Tripos. He also acquired, in the words of his son, 'exceptionally strong wrists, a legacy of college rowing at Cambridge'.

He is described as being fairly tall, about five foot eleven, slim and athletic, 'with looks as clean-cut as his ideas'. He had very clear and direct blue eyes – though his son was later to describe them as grey – a determined mouth, sharp nose, high forehead and very abundant black hair.

If his obituary in the *Daily Sketch* was correct in saying that he was at one time a schoolmaster, it must have been now, on coming down from Cambridge; and it is tempting to suppose that this occurred at Church Hill House in Crondall, since there is absolutely no record of the event.

CHAPTER IV

Crondall, pronounced either as Crondle or Crundle, was at this time a large, handsome village. Its streets were not yet paved and there was no electricity, save perhaps in the manor house itself. Cooking, lighting and heating were achieved with coal, wood, gas or oil. Sanitation, except in the very largest houses, was 'at the bottom of the garden'. The houses were mostly of brick, though some cottages were tile-hung, and dated from all centuries back to the sixteenth. The earlier roofs were tiled, the later ones of slate. The surviving photographs show it as being very neatly kept, an ideal village with a great deal of personal pride.

It had had a Fire Brigade since 1776 and a fire station, of which they were extremely proud, since 1883. The nineteenth century had contributed some large houses in their own grounds on the edge of the village, and at least one pub, the Plume of Feathers; but the village was still, at heart, the one laid out by the Saxons a thousand years previously. It seems to have existed in prosperity all that time, never deserted or destroyed, never overcome by industrial or agricultural revolution. The railway, however, had passed a few miles to the north. Visitors to Itchel Manor came by train to Farnham, where they were met by their hosts' fly or dog-cart.

Only Harold's sister Kathleen was at home. All the sons were scattered, the youngest recently sent off to the Naval College at

Osborne. So the question of Harold's future – he cannot have intended to remain a schoolmaster – must have been a frequent topic of conversation. One can imagine the bewildered question: 'But do tell me. What *is* an entymologist?'

And then, after the explanation: 'But, Harold, you surely don't mean a *bug*hunter?'

A bughunter, however, Harold was destined to be, and one of such distinction and influence that his contribution to the comfort of humanity, though sometimes indirect, can hardly be computed.

If the family, in which he seems to have been rather isolated, was surprised at having produced a first-class scientist with an original mind, they should perhaps have recalled that his maternal grandfather, Alfred Henry McClintock, had been a distinguished surgeon in Dublin; and that a paternal great-grandfather, James Walker, had been a civil engineer of enormous repute, involved in such lasting projects as Vauxhall Bridge, the river-wall of the Houses of Parliament, the sewers of London and the Thames Embankments. Any descendant of these gentlemen might reasonably be expected to have an enquiring mind, a talent for simple, effective solutions and, in particular, a desire to benefit humanity in his own individual way.

In 1895 Joseph Chamberlain, an energetic man who had made a fortune in industry in Birmingham, became Secretary of State for the Colonies. His attention was drawn to conditions in the West Indies, whose prosperity, largely based on the growing of sugar-cane, had been seriously undermined by the increase of refining beet sugar in Europe. They had also recently suffered a devastating drought. A royal commission was appointed, a consequence of which was the foundation of an Imperial Department of Agriculture in Barbados, with the future Sir Daniel Morris, from the Royal Botanic Gardens at Kew, as Commissioner. In that year, 1898, Barbados and the nearby islands of St Lucia and St Vincent were ravaged by a hurricane.

The British Government sent £40,000 in aid to the severely damaged islands and, in addition to this, 'a young entomologist from

Cambridge', as Sir Daniel Morris described him, was assigned to enquire particularly into the life-cycle of the Moth-borer, *Diatraea saccharalis*, an insect pest which had increasingly infested the sugar-cane crops during the previous two hundred years. He was to be paid an annual salary of £350 and travelling expenses of £100 a year. It can be assumed that this offer was accepted with alacrity and Harold arrived in Barbados at some time in 1899, after a sea journey of eleven days by Royal Mail steamer.

It did not take him very long to discover – what had escaped the attention of everyone else – that the Moth-borer laid its eggs on the undersides of the leaves of the sugar-cane. He also noticed that there were black eggs among the variously coloured ones, light yellow to orange brown. These black eggs he found to contain the eggs of a minute flying insect, *Trichogramma pretiosum*, eggs which destroyed the eggs of the Moth-borer. The first problem, therefore, was to destroy the eggs of the Moth-borer without also destroying its parasite.

It is the caterpillar of the Moth-borer which causes all the damage. On young cane plants it attacks the leaves, or the point where the leaves join the stem. On older plants it burrows into the stem itself, making tunnels up and down the plant. The caterpillar lives for thirty to thirty-five days, after which it spends six days as a pupa. It then emerges as a nocturnal moth, its upper wings buff, the lower wings of the male pale yellow, those of the female white. As a moth it lives for four days, during which it can lay up to three hundred eggs. In addition, a plant thus damaged by the Moth-borer becomes liable to attack by a fungus, *Colletotrichum falcatum*, which causes further, and frequently fatal, damage.

Harold's own account of his battle with the Moth-borer is to be found in Volume 1, No 4, of the *West Indian Bulletin*. He recommended that all the dried and diseased canes should be cut out and burnt as soon as possible after the harvest; that the new canes should be soaked in antiseptic before planting, to prevent rind fungus; that *all* the old stumps should be destroyed; that the moths themselves should be caught at night by surrounding trays of molasses with lamps; and that all the eggs collected should be put on plates encircled by molasses. In this case the caterpillars would get stuck on the molasses, while the *Trichogramma*, emerging as a winged insect, would be able to fly away. He mentions several other attempted remedies but dismisses them all as 'useless'.

His account ends with the laconic words: 'Planters must choose between getting all the sugar their land will yield, or letting the Moth-borer rob them of a large proportion of their canes.'

This, one of his first published utterances, is entirely characteristic of him. While it would not be true to say that the Moth-borer never appeared again in Barbados, it was never again allowed to become a pest.

Barbados is one of the most fertile of the Caribbean islands. It can be cultivated over 100,000 of its 106,470 acres. Its highest point, Mount Hillaby, rises to 1,100 feet in the centre of the island, all sides sloping gradually to the sea. The climate is pleasant, with temperatures rarely falling below 70, or rising above 86, degrees Fahrenheit. Named by the Spanish from the 'bearded' trees that they found there, the 'beard' most probably the epiphytic *Tillandsia* known as Spanish Moss in Florida, it was first successfully settled by English-speakers in 1625. Obliged to defend themselves from the French throughout the eighteenth century, and from the Americans early in the nineteenth, its history is peaceful thereafter. The transition of the slaves to paid workers was accomplished smoothly, in 1834.

Its principal scourge is cyclones, and the local jingle puts it thus:

June, too soon
July, stand by
August, look you must
September, remember
October, all over.

In fact there are almost as many hurricanes in October as there are in August.

Apart from asphalt, known as manjak, all the products of the island were then agricultural: rum, sugar and molasses from the sugar-cane, various kinds of fruit, cacao, coconuts and tobacco, all of them subject to one kind of insect pest or another. Harold set himself systematically to study them all. One notable result of his work, and his close association with Dr Daniel Morris, was the successful introduction of sea-island cotton as a profitable crop in 1903.

The Imperial Department of Agriculture was also responsible for other West Indian islands, Antigua, St Kitts, St Vincent, Dominica, Grenada, Montserrat, St Lucia, the Leeward Islands, the Virgin Islands and the Lesser Antilles. Harold seems to have visited them all.

An article in the *Official Gazette* of Barbados, under his initials, records an investigation of the sweet potato worm in St Lucia: 'Only stalks remain after the caterpillars have munched their way through the thick carpet' of vegetation.

A report from the Botanic Station in Antigua for 1901–2 states that: 'Mr. H. Maxwell-Lefroy, BA, FES, the Entomologist for the Imperial Department of Agriculture visited the island in May last, for the purpose of studying and suggesting remedies for various destructive insect pests.'

The Botanic Station in St Vincent reported in 1901:

Mr. H. Maxwell-Lefroy visited the island in August for the special purpose of investigating the caterpillar pest of the arrowroot which had re-appeared and was doing great damage in the Kingston and Leeward Districts. The Entomologist's Report was published in the Government Gazette. It is to be hoped that arrowroot growers will take advantage of the very valuable advice contained in it. Mr. Lefroy also investigated the mole cricket pest.

From the *Barbados Globe* we learn that:

Mr. H. Maxwell-Lefroy spent eleven days in Dominica in October. An interesting paper by him on the insect pests of the island was published in the Official Gazette.

Mr. H. Maxwell-Lefroy visited Montserrat in August 1901 and gave an address on Insect Pests. In his subsequent report he says: 'The total number of species of scale insects found is seventeen, a small number compared with what are found in other islands.'

He again visited St Lucia after a serious outbreak of the Screw-worm, which attacked pigs, sheep and cattle. He left a preliminary paper, in the form of a pamphlet, describing the nature of the pest and recommending that wounds caused by maggots should be cleaned, disinfected and dressed as the activities of the maggots caused blood-poisoning in the animals.

Harold wrote a great many pamphlets like, for instance, that on *The Scale Insects of the Lesser Antilles*. They all have the same pattern. The life history of the insect is followed by a careful description to make recognition easy. The methods of attack used by the insect are described, suggestions for preventing these attacks are made and a list of remedies actually available is given at the end. He contributed regularly to the *Barbados Bulletin* and was present at an exhibition in Bridgetown, on Wednesday the 17th of December 1900, to answer queries between 9 and 10 a.m. and again between 3 and 5 p.m.

In a circular note, on Black Blight, published in the *Official Gazette* in Bridgetown on the same day as the exhibition, he wrote:

> The insects and blights that attack ornamental plants and forest trees in this island have been studied by the officers of the Imperial Department of Agriculture during the past year. After a considerable amount of experiment a simple remedy has been found for a number of these pests and especially for those that cause the sooty appearance on the leaves of Mango trees and other plants. The Black Blight is not itself a disease, but is caused by attack of large numbers of small insects known as scale insects, mealy bugs and mealy wings...

The remedy is indeed simple. 'Whale oil soap has been found to be very efficacious in nearly all cases.' A pound of the soap is to be boiled in a gallon of water until dissolved, then cooled and applied with a spray. 'Borrow our machine,' he urges. 'We have two, one small hand, one large wheeled, for Mango, Orange, Lime, etc.' As a bonus, he adds: 'The whale oil soap contains the considerable fertilising properties of potash.'

A report from the Botanic Station in Grenada for 1902 and 1903, under the title of *Insecticides*, states that: 'Trees and shrubs, where attacked by insect pests, were regularly sprayed with cassbi potash and whale oil soap, kerosene emulsion and resin wash. Of these insecticides, whale oil soap has given the best result.'

The machines referred to in the circular note on Black Blight may well have been Harold's own inventions. In a pamphlet called *The General Treatment of Insect Pests*, which appeared under his name in two editions of April and October 1901, he gives illustrations of three machines then available in the United States: the 'Success' knapsack sprayer, the 'Fruitall' sprayer and the 'Gem' spraying outfit. He gives the addresses of suppliers, and prices, but there is no suggestion that any one of these machines has already arrived in Barbados. The second edition has a section on *Insectivorous Animals*, birds, lizards and toads, and both editions ask for specimens of insects to be collected and forwarded to him at the Department.

A list of recommended insecticides in the second edition is of interest. Two of what are called stomach poisons – those which would kill if taken internally – contain arsenic, Paris Green and London Purple. The other three are compounds of hellebore, pyrethrum and tobacco. The contact poisons, to be sprayed on, are kerosene emulsion, rosin wash, whale oil soap, rosin and soap mixture, tobacco and soap mixture and a rosin compound. Instructions for making up all these could be had from the Department.

By 1903 the successful activities of the Department of Agriculture in the West Indies had become well known. Dr Daniel Morris was later to claim that their methods had been adopted in India, the Malay States, on the Gold Coast and in southern Nigeria. In a book called *British Dominions*, published in 1911, he was to write:

Possibly in no direction have efforts of the Department been more successful than in encouraging a system of agricultural education among all classes of the community. All teachers in elementary schools have lectures and demonstrations in agriculture; agricultural training schools for boys have been established in St. Vincent, St. Lucia and Dominica. Scientific and agricultural teaching is available in secondary schools and colleges. Local departments of agriculture have been established in British Guiana, Jamaica and Trinidad.

Harold's devotion to his work, his lucidly written pamphlets, his enthusiasm and knowledge, the openness of his mind in seeking more knowledge and, above all, the certainty that anything he recommended had been tried and tested by himself, had established his reputation as someone who knew precisely what he was doing. Seldom, if ever, could a pioneer in any comparable field have achieved such remarkable results with such simple methods. In that year, 1903, he was appointed Entomologist to the Government of India.

Of the circumstances of his own life during this time we know nothing. If he wrote letters to his parents they have not survived. Did he live *en pension* in a small hotel? Possibly, in the fashion of those days, he had a landlady who cooked and washed and sewed; perhaps he rented a small house with a cook and a manservant. What we do know is that he was a member of at least one club, because it was at a club that he first met Miss Kathleen Hamilton O'Meara.

She was one of the three daughters of William O'Meara, originally from Roscrea, Co. Tipperary, a former Provost Marshal in British Guiana, and his wife Lucy. They also had a son, Arthur. They had retired to the benevolent climate of Barbados after enduring the exhausting, stifling heats of Georgetown, where Kathleen was born. She is described as neither very tall nor very small, vivacious and courageous, with large blue eyes and an abundance of beautiful brown hair. Her first impression of him, when seen at that club, was that 'he looked very lonely and ill-at-ease.'

Before he set sail for England they were engaged to be married.

CHAPTER V

The engagement was not well received at home.

Kathleen O'Meara was Roman Catholic, Irish, quite literally from beyond the Pale, and colonial into the bargain. She brought no money. As daughter-in-law to a socially ambitious woman she would not do. The principal objection, however, as befitted descendants of Antoine l'Offroy, was to her Catholicism. Her son records:

> During his youth, my father obediently went to the local church in Crondall and to school chapel at Marlborough, but religion took no root in his mind and he quickly 'opted out'. My mother made no attempt to convert him, while he respected her wish to bring up her children as Catholics, which was indeed a pre-condition for the Vatican's grant of permission for the mixed marriage to take place. It would have mattered as little to him had she been a Zoroastrian.

To two members of his family it seems to have mattered a great deal. Harold's immediately elder brother Jack and his sister Kathleen both decided to have nothing further to do with him should the marriage take place. But, as the bride of an entomologist on his way to India, Kathleen O'Meara was more than just eminently suitable. She was already accustomed to heat, to all the discomforts and inconveniences of colonial life and, inevitably, to insects. She had a sense of humour strong enough to surmount most obstacles. The engagement held.

Harold's employment agreement, as a Government Entomologist, was signed at the India Office in London on the 7th of March 1903, in the presence of Mr Frank Marten. The signatories were Harold himself, his father, and two members of the Council of India, Sir Philip Percival Hutchins, Knight Commander of the Star of India, and Lieutenant-General Sir Alexander Robert Badcock, Knight Commander of the Bath and of the Star of India.

These were people of importance. The contract must have been negotiated at the highest level and here one may again detect the hand of Dr David Sharp, still Curator of Insects at Cambridge. It was he who recommended Harold for his position in Barbados and there can be no doubt that his influence was now exerted once more. It is also possible that the results of Harold's activities in the West Indies had become known at the India Office, since these could by now be computed in terms of increased production, increased prosperity and, therefore, increased revenue.

His contract was for five years, with no home leave. He was required to learn one of the Indian languages (depending entirely on which part of India he found himself in) and be examined in it. A failure here would result in loss of salary and seniority, possibly in dismissal. He was to devote himself entirely to the service of government, and not engage directly or indirectly in trade, business or occupation on his own account. This meant, in particular, that all his written work was the property of that Government. He was not to absent himself from his duties without first obtaining permission.

His salary was to be 750 rupees a month, rising each year by 50 rupees a month to a final total of 1,000 rupees a month. An annual salary of 12,000 rupees was about equivalent to £1,000 a year at that time. His fare to India, £50 First Class, was to be paid by the Government of India, but this would have to be paid back should he fail to complete his contract.

Harold sailed from Tilbury on the Peninsular & Oriental steamer *Borneo* on the 27th of March. He was never again to see his father, neither is there any reason to suppose that he ever again set foot inside Itchel Manor. He arrived in Calcutta, having disembarked at Bombay, on the 30th of April 1903.

On the 2nd of April a letter was sent to him from the India Office, informing him that he had been attached to the Agricultural Department under the Inspector General of Agriculture, to whom he should report his arrival by telegram, and that instructions regarding his work would be communicated to him by the Inspector.

On that same date, a letter was sent to the Secretary of the Trustees of the Indian Museum in Calcutta, announcing Harold's appointment and that his headquarters were to be for the present in Calcutta. It requested office accommodation in the Museum and asked Mr Stebbing, the Forestry Entomologist, to give him every possible assistance.

The Indian Museum was a massive stone edifice in the Italian style, completed in 1875. It was entirely funded by the Government of India. It housed collections of Indian archaeology and natural history; the records of the Society of Bengal were kept there; and the Geological Survey and the Asiatic Society had offices there.

It is tempting to think that the authorities still viewed entomologists as desiccated old men sticking pins in dead beetles before putting them away for ever in glass-topped drawers. If the expression 'economic entomology' had been heard in such circles it was no doubt regarded as a contradiction in terms. The arrival of a man of twenty-six, enthusiastic, very much alive, energetic and even rather handsome, must have caused a certain amount of surprise.

Shortly after Harold's death, Professor E.P. Stebbing, then Professor of Forestry at Edinburgh, wrote to *The Times*:

> …on arrival at Bombay early in 1903 Lefroy discovered that little was known about his appointment as Imperial Entomologist. At the time, I was holding the officiating post of Superintendent of the Indian Museum, Calcutta. A few weeks later I received a semi-official letter from one of the Under-Secretaries in Simla saying that Lefroy had been instructed to

report to me at the Indian Museum, and asking me to assist the newcomer in any way possible and let him start work in the Insect Department of the Museum.

This must have been about April, 1903, and I have always looked back with pleasure to the few months Lefroy spent with me. Without exception he was the keenest and most enthusiastic man I have ever met. In his nine years in India he revolutionised all previous methods of studying the insect pests of agricultural crops, and, with the assistance of capable staff, he carried out an amazing amount of careful study and research into life histories of many serious pests, suggesting what were, perhaps, the first practical and feasible remedies ever adumbrated in India. Agricultural research was fortunate, at its inception by the late Lord Curzon, in securing on the Institute's staff many able men. But his colleagues would, I think, support me in saying that there was none abler or more of a 'live wire' than Lefroy…

Harold must have received his letter from the India Office on leaving the ship in Bombay. He would then have had to travel by train to Calcutta, a journey of about forty-eight hours. He is said to have announced his arrival after working hours and to have begun work immediately.

British India was a very large place, some 2,300 miles at its widest, east to west, and 2,000 at its longest, north to south. It included the present-day countries of Pakistan, Bangladesh and Burma and its population, in 1903, was 350,000,000.

It consisted of three enormous Presidencies, Bengal, Bombay and Madras; and four provinces, Burma, the Central Provinces and Berar, the Punjab and the recently formed (1902) United Provinces of Agra and Oudh. With the partition of Bengal in 1905, two new provinces were to appear, Eastern Bengal and Assam and Bihar and Orissa, though these were later to be divided again.

The Governors of the Presidencies were, in general, political appointments from London; the others came from within the ranks of the Indian Civil Service. Each of these areas had their own languages, with their own scripts. At least two hundred languages were in use in India at that time.

There were also the so-called Native States, ruled by their own Maharaja, Nizam or Gaekwar, under the eye of a British Resident or Agent. Certain districts – the North-West Frontier Province, for instance, British Baluchistan or Coorg – had a Chief Commissioner rather than a Governor.

In the north lay the hidden, forbidden Himalayan kingdoms of Nepal and Bhutan, with the Native State of Sikkim sandwiched between them, giving access from the south to Tibet. At a high point in the Pamirs in the north-west, three empires met, the Indian, the Russian and the Chinese, and the most pressing threat to the peace of India was considered to come from the Russians. The great fear, which underlay the Great Game, was that they would invade Afghanistan and then annexe the North-West Frontier Province.

The supreme authority in India was the Viceroy, also a political appointment from London; but in any serious dispute with the Council of India, or with the Secretary of State for India in London, the Viceroy might find himself obliged to give way.

The Viceroy at this time was George Nathaniel, Lord Curzon, known since his Oxford days as 'a most superior person'. He had first arrived in India as Viceroy at the end of December 1898, accompanied by his beautiful American wife, the former Mary Victoria Leiter of Chicago, one of the heiresses to the Marshall Field fortune.

The Viceroy's headquarters were in Calcutta, also capital of the Bengal Presidency. Between April and the end of September the Viceregal Court moved to Simla, a hill station in the Punjab, between 6,600 and 8,000 feet high in the Himalayas, and more than a thousand miles from Calcutta. In the year that Harold arrived in India, it was possible to do the whole journey by train.

For eight to ten weeks after the monsoon was over, the Viceroy went 'on tour', travelling principally in his special train, a unique and magnificent conveyance painted in white and gold. Then he returned to Calcutta for Christmas.

While the political consequences of Curzon's administration may now be subject to some re-assessment, it must be admitted that he was able to benefit, at ground level, an enormous section of the population. In one of the last speeches he made in India, at the Byculla Club in Bombay, he said: 'The sense of being able to do something, to effect some good, to leave something better than you found it, is a perpetual incentive and consolation.'

His efforts, many of them very successful, to improve agriculture, education, irrigation and transport, should be considered in that light. He was the first Viceroy to make it clear to those in trade, the *boxwallahs*, both Indian and European, that he believed their existence to be the foundation on which the Indian Empire was built. One of his great achievements was to create a sixth place on the Viceroy's Council, for the Department of Industry and Commerce.

In the field of agriculture, Curzon's administration had begun badly. A fierce famine in 1896–97 had affected the whole of central India, from Bihar to the Punjab, and in 1899, his first year of office, the monsoon, the south-west wind which brings rain to India between May and October and on which the agriculture of the whole country depends, had failed.

By October 1900 there was what he described as 'a fodder famine on an enormous scale' and the lives of sixty million people were at stake. It drew his attention to the need for further irrigation, improved agriculture and changes in the system of land tenure. In time he was to achieve them all.

There had been Agricultural Departments in all the provinces since the 1880s. There were four experimental farms, at Poona, Surat, Nadiad and Kirkee, all in the Presidency of Bombay. These now tended to be both unscientific and inefficient, languishing perhaps for lack of interest and lack of funds. In 1901 Curzon established the Imperial Agricultural Department, with an Inspector General at its head, Mr J.W. Mollison, a Canadian. He began to collect a staff of scientific experts and the discussion began, as we learn from the India Office files, as to where the principal research station should be located.

Eyes were very soon turned towards a vacant estate of about 1280 acres at Pusa, in northern Bihar, which had belonged to the Government since 1796. It had most recently been used by a tobacco-growing firm, which had built a factory and three handsome bungalows, but their lease had expired in 1897. At first, Mr Mollison did not think it suitable for all their purposes; the uplands were 'uneven' and suitable for cattle and dairy work only. He noted, however, that the ground was extremely fertile, as was evidenced by the proportions of the shade trees, and the excellence of the grass. A river, the Burh Gandak, offered a natural boundary.

Mr G. W. Watt, Director of the Indian Museum, on the other hand, was in favour of Pusa. 'Improvement in stock is the most powerful direction in which a research station can advance the agricultural interests of India.'

He thought the site could, and should, be used for research into sugar-cane, indigo, cotton and silk. His concern was largely administrative, offering practical suggestions as to how the Research Station should be run. Notably, he did not think that the Entomologist and the Mycologist (Fungi) should be resident. They could be consulted when required.

Reports dated February and March 1901 suggest that one particular area of the land would be suitable for rice. Experiments with wheat, barley, sugar-cane, ginger, turmeric, potatoes, sweet potatoes, ground nuts and various indigenous fodder crops could be conducted on other parts of it. The surroundings to the bungalows were suitable as botanical gardens, and experiments could be carried out with fruit trees.

In March it was decided that the Research Station would definitely be located at Pusa and we may suppose that the work of repairing the bungalows, clearing the land and putting it into working order began then.

A Government Entomologist had already been appointed to the Indian Museum, but he had died in December 1901 of malaria, an endemic disease whose source, as far as the human being was concerned, had only recently (1899) been traced to the female anopheline mosquito. The question of his successor now arose and in January 1902 Mr E.P. Stebbing is found to be saying that an entomologist *in the office* is not what is required, but someone with a sufficiently sound scientific training – that is to say outside entomology – and a knowledge of agriculture sufficiently wide for him to be able to propose remedies that can easily be put into practise. He described work then being undertaken in the USA. It is possible that Harold's work in the West Indies now came under scrutiny from the India Office.

Matters came to a head in the Cold Weather of 1902–3. A wealthy American, Mr Henry Phipps, whom we may assume to have been a friend of the Vicereine as he was travelling with the Curzons, and who may well have witnessed the Great Durbar in Delhi in January, was so impressed by Lord Curzon's determination to improve the welfare of the people of India that he offered him a private gift of £20,000 to be spent on any project which would permanently benefit the Indian people. This was later increased to £30,000. After some deliberation, Lord Curzon decided that this money should be given to the Agricultural Research Centre at Pusa.

On the 19th of January 1903, Mr Phipps telegraphed to Lord Curzon: 'I am much pleased with the excellent choice you have made. In my judgement none could be better…May I add that your ability, devotion to duty and solicitude for the welfare of the natives, have influenced me in the step I am taking.'

As it had by now been decided that a Resident Entomologist was required at Pusa, this was to be Harold's eventual destination. In the meantime, however, Mr Mollison decreed that he would be of more use on the Bombay farms than elsewhere. 'The experimental work and crops are much more varied there than in other provinces, and the general cultivation in the vicinity of the farms will enable him to see most of the Indian field and garden crops much sooner than in other provinces.'

On the 30th of June, the Secretary to the Government of India informed the Governors of Madras, Bombay, Bengal, the United Provinces, the Punjab and Burma, the Chief Commissioners of the Central Provinces and Assam, of Ajmer-Merwara and Coorg, and the Honourable the Resident at Hyderabad that Harold Maxwell-Lefroy had replaced the late Mr de Nicéville as Government Entomologist and that he would in future be attached to the Agricultural Department.

The Indian Museum had first published its *Notes on Economic Entomology*, on Rice and Wheat Weevils, in 1888. Thereafter they were called *Indian Museum Notes* and by this time they contained a wealth of information, in five volumes, with fifty-six excellent plates. Having perused these with care, and having suggested to Mr Stebbing that he issue a number of illustrated circulars on the more frequent insect pests of India – as he was afterwards to do – Harold took another long train journey to Surat, 167 miles north of Bombay, on the Bombay, Baroda and Central Indian Railway.

This was the first English settlement in India, wrested from the Portuguese in 1612 and, before the acquisition of Bombay in the dowry of Queen Catherine of Braganza in 1661 – *bom bahia* being the Portuguese for 'good bay' – a very important port. Surat had cotton mills and rice mills and behind it lay a rich, highly cultivated plain bounded, on the north-east, by the Thana Hills. The Experimental Farms were principally concerned with garden crops, onions, wheat and cotton, the establishment of a manure rotation system and experiments with various irrigated crops.

Here Harold must have begun to understand that insects were by no means his only problem. He had a place in a rigid hierarchy and he was expected to stay in it. In Barbados everyone had spoken English and everyone was, at least nominally, Christian. In the words of a Confidential Report from the Department of Land Records in February 1901: 'In India we require demonstration as a supplement to research. We have to deal with uneducated native labour, ultra conservative and almost penniless. He is on the whole contented with his present position, adverse to innovation, and his only criterion for experimental work is financial advantage.'

Over the centuries, the Indian small farmer had become accustomed to the varied behaviour of the Hindu gods and he was very reluctant to provoke them. The taking of life, even the lives of potentially injurious insects, was not a thing he would do lightly.

From Harold's Report for 1903 we learn:

> While I was on tour in August and September, villagers near Surat reported an insect attacking cabbages. I sent my field man to investigate. He sprayed with insecticide and the crop became healthy, while the unsprayed plants did not. The villagers were impressed and promised to do it themselves the next time. The field man can go to the district without exciting distrust, as the appearance of the Entomologist appears to do. He convinced people that no harm would be done, and was successful in showing villagers how they can save their own crops. This is the practical realization of work hitherto done by the Entomologist, and it is precisely this class of work I expect the trained native to do.

In November, he was shown a crop which, as he realised at once, had been almost destroyed by aphids, greenfly. He was told that the insects doing the damage had been collected, and these proved to be a kind of ladybird, one of the greenfly's greatest natural enemies. In a letter to his Inspector General he emphasised again the need for specially trained men at that level. 'My own work at the present time would be trebly effective had I the assistance of such trained men familiar with the crops and the Presidency.'

Locusts were causing a great deal of trouble, though they were to cause a great deal more in the following year.

> If any measures are to be undertaken against locusts it must be when they are young and wingless. They must be found and dealt with. I trust it may be possible next year to use trained men. For the next years it may be necessary to employ trained men in August and September only on locust work and by then village officers can be left to the work themselves.

In November an Ideal Hammond typewriter was installed in his office in Surat. A microscope, which Harold had arranged to have sent to him at his own expense, was mistakenly confiscated and kept by the Inspector General of Agriculture. He seems to have been in dispute with the authorities about who was to pay for his *peons*, his office messengers. He did not take kindly to hierarchies.

Then, very early in 1904, he requested that arrangements be made for him to receive his salary at Surat, rather than at Bombay. This was declined. It was 'not the usual procedure'. He was not classified as 'peripatetic staff', although he was at this time drawing a travel allowance of 9,000 rupees a year, exactly equal to his salary.

On the 22nd of January 1904 Harold married Kathleen O'Meara at the Cathedral of the Holy Name in Bombay. There was no requirement for residence on the part of the bride in British India; she would have been married 'off the ship'. The bridegroom is described as English, aged twenty-seven, domiciled at Surat; the bride as Irish, twenty-four, domiciled in Barbadoes, West Indies.

The ceremony was performed by Father Joseph George, SJ, in the presence of Tom Lawson Roberts, of Bombay, and Lucy O'Meara, the bride's younger sister. We may suppose that the two sisters travelled together, chaperoning each other.

> My mother realised full well that she might have to compete in his affections for an already deeply rooted 'first love' – entomology. In fact there was ample room for both in the hearts and minds of two outstanding characters and they remained devoted to each other right until his premature end.

There is no suggestion of a honeymoon. We can only suppose that they went straight to Surat, where Harold had by now had time to make himself reasonably comfortable; and we must also suppose, for lack of any other information, that Lucy went with them.

CHAPTER VI

In February 1904 Harold's first Indian assistant was appointed. He was Mr P. Ukkadanunni Nair, MA, a twenty-seven-year-old zoologist from the Christian College in Madras.

In March Harold wrote to the Inspector General about the state of the collections in the Indian Museum. These were in such total confusion as to be unusable and many of the specimens were in fact beyond identification. He asked for an assistant, either a European or an Indian whom he could train. Without such an assistant he was unable to help the Museum and it was unable to help him. He also suggested changes to *Indian Museum Notes*, including that of a new title.

This correspondence spilled over into September, when he wrote to ask if he should prepare the first number of *Entomology Notes*, and sent it to the Inspector General for printing.

'Please get authority for all drawings, blocks, plates, to be transferred to me so that I may use the illustrations.'

But, to begin with at least, 1904 was to be the Year of the Locusts.

The Bombay Locust, *Acridium succinctum*, lays its eggs in June, in the wildernesses of the Thana Hills. They hatch in July and the wingless hopper – the nymph – goes through five to seven moults before emerging as a winged adult – the imago – in September. Only then does it swarm. It lives until the following June, when it lays its eggs, between a hundred and a hundred and twenty, and then it dies.

The Migratory Locust, *Acridium peregrinum*, on the other hand, lays its eggs in open, sandy plains and it does so twice a year. Its hoppers at once form themselves into armies, marching together in serried ranks. Entirely herbivorous, they eat anything, everything, on their way. In Harold's own words: 'Locusts have a very wide range of food plants.'

Swarms of locusts had been observed in the Thana Hills in the previous Hot Weather. They had attacked standing crops throughout the autumn and winter, but in April and May were found, in the western Deccan (in the Bombay Presidency), to be dying in huge numbers, either from disease or – a situation which almost defies the imagination – from starvation. Nevertheless, they were continuing to breed, particularly in the hills known as the Western Ghats, south of Surat.

Harold and another entomologist, a Mr Knight, presumably from the Presidency, were deputed to leave all other work and concentrate on the problem.

Indian locusts, generally speaking, are destructive principally in the dry areas, since only there do they breed. A notable swarm, mentioned in Cuvier's *Natural History* of 1832 and quoted in *Indian Insect Life*, was thought to have come from Arabia. 'The column extended five hundred miles, and was so dense as thoroughly to hide the sun, and prevent any object from casting a shadow.'

As the local inhabitants expected locusts, to which they were perfectly accustomed, to descend from the air, it proved particularly difficult to convince them that they laid eggs in the sand and that the hoppers would eventually develop wings; but, to an extent, Harold and Mr Knight succeeded.

They sprayed, destroying the adult locusts on the trees, two thousand at a time. They collected eggs, about three million. They caught the coupling adults at night. They rounded up and destroyed the hoppers by what is described as the 'bag method', enticing them in, perhaps, or trawling for them. Rewards were offered, possibly not quite large enough, because in the end the villagers would do no more. They were tired of digging for eggs and counting hoppers and were by no means convinced that they were destroying locusts.

The attack was contained, at a cost of some £14,000. Various sprays were tried out, some successful, some ineffectual. The local populace had been involved and the point was made that, with anti-locust campaigns in August and September, and in particular with trained native entomologists, home-produced locusts need never again be a menace.

The episode seems to have established that the function of the entomologist was both practical and important. A report from the Bengal Agriculture Department invites 'the attention of District Officers to the necessity of having insect pests occurring in their districts identified by the Entomologist'. He would be able to suggest remedies in many cases.

At Pusa, the arrangements progressed. Mr Bernard Coventry, an indigo planter from Bihar, originally brought in to supervise all the work, was now appointed Director of the Research Institute and Principal of the Agricultural College, in April. Indigo, which had replaced woad as the sole source of blue dye in the seventeenth century, was now in its turn being replaced by the synthetic dyes of the late nineteenth century. It had no other function – as it could not be eaten – and very shortly ceased to be grown except for botanical interest.

In June Mr Mollison, the Inspector General, received an honorarium of 1,500 rupees for his *Text Book on Indian Agriculture*, a work of three volumes, the copyright remaining with the Government. In September he forwarded to that Government an advance copy of a bulletin which Harold had written, on the *Insect Pests of Coffee in South India*, so we may assume a journey to Mysore in this year. Then, in October, Mr Mollison wrote again:

> Maxwell-Lefroy has done a good deal of useful entomological work which affects the agriculture of Western and Central India. He has given advice on practical remedies for injurious insects and otherwise has done

---

a good deal of demonstration work. I asked him to go to Bihar recently to observe injurious insects affecting

(1) the varieties of cotton under experiment

(2) the more general crops at Pusa and elsewhere cultivated in Bengal.

Considering the advancement of his work in Western India and the need for his services in connection with work more directly in the control of my Department I have thought it necessary to ask him to make his HQ at Mozufferpore. He will work from this centre until he can be accommodated at Pusa.

So, possibly in November, Harold and Kathleen moved from Surat to Muzaffarpur (in a later spelling), a thousand-mile journey by train with many changes. It seems to have been a pleasant place, laid out along two lakes and surrounded by spreading ricefields, dotted with clumps of giant bamboo and groves of mango trees. It was a busy town, on the main trade route to Nepal, and about thirty miles from Pusa.

Harold's letter about the inadequacies of the Indian Museum now bore fruit. The Inspector General forwarded the correspondence to Government, virtually endorsing all Harold's requests. The Entomologist was to select a suitable assistant at the Museum, whose business it would be to identify, classify and arrange all the existing specimens; the Entomologist would supply duplicates from his own collection to the Museum; all notes, drawings, etc. and the artist staff were to be placed at the Entomologist's disposal; and *Indian Museum Notes* would be re-titled *Notes on Entomology*. The Inspector General himself would scrutinise each issue at its proof stage.

Harold's salary had been transferred from the Museum to the Department of Agriculture in the previous year. To these proposals the Trustees of the Museum were later to reply that, as they would be paying the suggested assistant, they should be able to choose him; and, as they would also be paying for the publication of *Indian Museum Notes*, they could not agree to the change of title. They did agree, however, that the editorship should pass to the Entomologist and they accepted all the other proposals.

That this matter was very close to Harold's heart is shown by a letter to the Inspector General, dated the 8th of December 1904 from Muzaffarpur:

> I would suggest that the question of publication is an important one, and that the procedure should be settled. A great mass of information lies in my office awaiting publication and though I am not desirous of publishing in a hurry it would facilitate the preparation of reports, etc. if I knew when and in what form the reports would be published. I have previously pointed out that some useful information on Economic Entomology is published in Annual Reports of Farms and other places where one would not look for it, e.g. Mr. Hayman's *Notes on Cotton Pests* in Annual Report of Cawnpore Farm just issued. These should in my opinion be gathered in one publication available to everyone and where every officer would look for such information.

The year closed on an encouraging note in a report from the Punjab. An Indian Agricultural Assistant, after some training at Pusa, had now started to work by himself, studying insect pests in the country near Lahore. He was to forward his specimen monthly reports to Harold himself and visit him for a fortnight every year. During this time, any collections he had made would be identified, they would discuss his progress and he would receive any assistance that he needed.

Harold's enthusiasm and vast knowledge, just as he wished, now began to be shared. There must have been a considerable feeling of satisfaction there.

On the 6th of January 1905, the first meeting of the Board of Agriculture took place at Pusa. Harold is recorded as having agreed to go to Assam, in the north-east, at the suggestion of the Assam Department, to demonstrate his investigations into their indigenous insects. He also gave information about two serious rice pests in Bengal which were 'engaging his attention'.

But the main discussion of interest to him was about the growing of cotton.

The British Cotton Growing Association had recently written to the Government of India expressing its concern about the low quality of cotton grown in India. They offered financial help for its improvement, help that was already being given to the West Indies and to East and West Africa. They now proposed that experimental farms should be set up to try and improve the standard of the indigenous crop. Imported strains were to be tried again, even though those previously tested had not been successful.

Almost the entire cotton crop of the United States had been destroyed by the Cotton Boll Weevil in the previous year. The infestations in imported seeds were already known to be causing enormous damage. These were matters which would shortly engage Harold's attention very closely.

There were by now between twenty and thirty Europeans at Pusa, including their families. Mr E. Shearer, the Agriculture Horticulturalist, was to give his son, born in 1915, the names Harold Maxwell Lefroy. The Imperial Mycologist was Dr E.J. Butler. Mr Albert Howard was the Biological Botanist. Mr Bernard Coventry must have been resident there and possibly Mr Mollison, although this is not clear.

One resident whose name must be mentioned, if only rather sadly, was Gladys Elizabeth, Harold and Kathleen's first child, who lived for a few months in 1905. The precise cause of her death is not known.

There were between two hundred and fifty and three hundred Indian staff of various kinds, research assistants, laboratory assistants, fieldmen, clerks and house servants. Mr Nair had been found not up to his job and he had been replaced by Mr S.C. Misra.

On the 1st of April Lord Curzon himself arrived to lay the foundation stone of the Phipps Research Laboratory at Pusa. He was accompanied by the Lieutenant Governor of Bengal, Sir Denzil Ibbetson, and the ceremony was performed under a huge *shamiana*, a kind of triumphal canopy, a decorated tent without sides. The Viceroy received addresses from the Bihar Indigo Planters' Association and from the Bihar Landowners' Association. In his speech, before laying the stone, he said:

The original idea was to have just a laboratory, then a research laboratory within an experimental farm. But if the results of our experiments are to be of practical value they must be brought home to the cultivator, whose mind must be prepared to receive them by a modicum of education in the rationale of that agriculture he practises so skilfully and so blindly. Agricultural science at present exists only in European languages. To reach the cultivator we must translate it into the vernacular. We want teachers and we want text-books. Men competent to instruct the one and compile the other have still to be trained. We have added therefore an Agricultural College of a high class, fitted to complete the training which the Provincial Colleges will begin.

Pusa's threefold object was to conduct research in the laboratory, experiment in the field and instruction in the classroom.

The Commissioner of the Patna Division of the day, who was of course also present, is recorded as saying that the speech made a profound impression on everyone who heard it. Lord Curzon was at this time deadlocked in a battle with the future Lord Kitchener which led, at the end of the year, to Curzon's resignation.

Attempting to keep the peace between them was a Bishop Lefroy, soon to be Metropolitan Bishop of Calcutta. He was one of the Irish Lefroys who, with three of his brothers, had been to Marlborough some years before Harold. It was his name that was given, along with those of Ibbetson and Curzon, to a house at Bishop Cotton's School for Boys in Simla. There is no suggestion that he and Harold ever met in India.

The re-establishment of a silk industry in India had been one of Harold's most cherished projects ever since his arrival in India. An old industry had been allowed to decline and the Japanese and the Chinese had captured the international markets. The so-called silkworm is, in fact, the larva of a moth which, approaching its stage as a pupa, surrounds itself with a cocoon made from a single thread wound round its body. This thread, unwound and reeled, can achieve a length of twelve hundred yards and it is this which makes the silk.

Three silk-producing moths are native to India, all indigenous to the Brahmaputra Valley, where they formed bases for cottage industries. They are the Eri Moth, *Attacus ricini*, the Muga Moth, *Antheraea assama*, and the Tasar Moth, *Antheraea paphia*. The first of these was already semi-domesticated, while the other two were only to be found wild, living off the forest trees. As those particular forests could not be re-created anywhere else in India – the climate of Assam being unique – these small industries did not allow of much development. The Chinese Silkworm, *Bombyx mori*, on the other hand, existed only in cultivation and could in theory be reared wherever its sole food, the White Mulberry, *Morus alba*, could be grown.

A plantation of these mulberry trees some ten acres in extent had already been laid out at Pusa and they were now ready to start the rearing of silkworms, under the eye of the Government Entomologist. The great Parsee industrialist, Sir Dorabji Jamsetji Tata, who was also extremely interested in reviving the silk industry, had found a Japanese expert and had agreed to pay for him. He arrived with his wife, an expert reeler, and an interpreter, on a contract for five years.

Plans were now under discussion between the Inspector General and the Government for a *Quarterly Journal* of a very high quality, to cover agricultural chemistry and bacteriology, botany, mycology and entomology. A series of scientific *Memoirs* were to be published separately.

The *Journal* was carefully estimated and the budget presented, including the extra staff required, a clerk and proof-reader, a typist, an artist and an assistant artist, a photographer and a *peon* who were, between them, to be paid 5,500 rupees a year. In August, Government replied that they were not very sanguine about the success of this project, but they approved it for three years. They suggested that the Inspector General should retain the Editorship, merely *consulting* the various experts.

So widely had Harold's fame spread by this time that he was no longer able to deal, alone, with all the queries that came flooding in from all parts of India. He applied for an assistant to specialise in all problems relating to moths. In June a Mr Dudgeon, supernumerary on the Museum staff, who had met Harold earlier in the year, was now appointed from London for three years. He was on probation, however, to which Mr Dudgeon not surprisingly objected, and was not to be given free accommodation, about which he also protested. Although his complaints were disallowed, he did arrive in Pusa and no doubt went with Harold on many of his field trips.

These field trips are, disappointingly enough, not very well documented. Possibly Government was not interested in details at ground level. But there is one short account of spraying with a Success Knapsack Spraying Machine, of which there were only three in the whole area, and which took five hours to spray one acre. Two men were needed, as the labour was heavy, and two women to carry water from the nearest pond. They used 120 gallons of liquid and between three and five pounds of Paris Green, an arsenical compound. Harold wrote: 'There is no doubt as to the efficacy of the treatment. On inspecting a field where Paris Green had been applied the day before, it was found that the caterpillars were unable to withstand the treatment, many were dead and those which remained alive were unable to eat and appeared unwell.'

The crop can only be guessed at, but it was in all probability cotton. This would have been a slow, though not particularly expensive, method of disposing of the Boll Weevil, as two acres was the maximum to be sprayed in one day by a team of four.

Numbers of field trips were made throughout the year, doubtless as many as Harold could contrive as they were one of his first interests; but a great deal of his time, and all his spare time, must have been spent in the preparation of his first book, *Indian Insect Pests*, which was to be published in May of the following year.

CHAPTER VII

At the beginning of 1906, not long after the death of her daughter, Kathleen gave birth to a healthy son, Denis Charles, who successfully survived the perils of infancy in India.

They must by now have been living in the 'compound' at Pusa, possibly in one of the old bungalows built by the tobacco firm. 'Upcountry' bungalows, in the *mofussil*, tended to be built to the same plan, only the details and the pitch of the roof varying from district to district. There was a wide verandah – itself an Indian word – along the front or round three sides of the house. The sitting-room, with a bedroom on either side, led off it. Behind the sitting-room would be the dining room, with the two rear bedrooms leading out of it. There were no corridors. Enormous *punkahs*, oblong fans of frilled cloth, hung from the ceiling on a pulley, operated from the verandah by a servant. These, at least, kept the warm air circulating.

Each bedroom had its own bathroom, opening to the great outdoors, the outside door left open for the sweeper to come in and take away the used thunder-box or chamber pot. What he did with the contents was his own secret, but it is improbable that they were buried. The cookhouse was always a separate building, sometimes joined to the house by a covered way. It was by no means unknown for food to disappear between the two buildings, at the hands of marauding monkeys, or in the talons of a hungry kite. Behind the dining room would be the butler's pantry, the *bottlekhana*, where the food waited to be served; and it was here, if the flies were going to get at it, that they did so.

In January 1906, the officiating Inspector General requested electrical installations at Pusa, in particular for lighting and fans in the public buildings, and in the bungalows if the occupants would pay for the installation. Water piped into the buildings is almost a certainty at this time; efficient laboratories could scarcely function without it, but it may not have been included even in the new bungalows. Water-closets seem unlikely, since water, in spite of the proximity of the river, would have been a problem at Pusa for six months in the year, possibly for the whole of the dry season.

The Government Entomologist's *Report on Pests in the Punjab* for 1905 includes descriptions of the ravages of the Cotton Bollworm and the Semi-looper Caterpillar. Their life histories are described and their parasites listed, 'trap crops' are suggested and the habits of the Cotton Mealy Bug are detailed. A serious campaign against the insect pests of cotton in the Punjab was planned for the coming season.

An enquiry about introducing pests to destroy 'nut grass', a noxious weed in Madras, was not encouraged. 'The elements of danger outweigh the advantages. Once introduced, insect pests cannot be controlled and can become a scourge.'

There are notes from him and Dr Butler on the insect and fungus pests of wheat and tobacco and a way of discovering damaged cotton seed is mentioned. After rubbing the fuzz, which surrounds the seed, with a mixture of earth and cow dung, the seeds are thrown into water. The useless seeds will float. A new insectary – a place for keeping live insects – is asked for at Pusa, in addition to the existing one and he asks for a new field cage, to help him discover 'Where and for how long do insect pests hibernate?' The experimental cage cost 380 rupees, the revised one would cost 480. 'I would like to erect ten at Pusa. The money would be well spent.'

The library claimed his attention.

Pusa must be the headquarters of Entomology and a proper reference library is essential. We are cut off from the resources of Europe and must have a substitute. I ask definitely for an increase in the annual grant for books, a lump sum now of Rs. 25,000. The present grants are on my budget Rs. 500 and on the 2nd Entomologist's for the first year Rs. 1,500. Annual grants should be at least Rs. 1,500 for each of us. If a lump sum cannot be granted, an annual grant of Rs. 5,000 is required to keep us up to date with our work.

He asks once more for another European entomologist at Pusa, to concentrate, in particular, on research into the subject of the insects' own enemies.

Work on his book was now sufficiently advanced for it to have received an estimate from the printer.

The material has accumulated during the last four years. It has been worked up in the form of notes and is now a fairly complete text book. It is not expected to sell at a profit, and I therefore ask for a grant of Rs. 12,000 to pay expenses, on the understanding that copies required by the Government for use by Imperial and Provincial Agricultural Depts. will be free, and that the proceeds of sale on all other copies shall accumulate as an honorarium for myself.

The estimate from Thacker, Spink of Calcutta was Rs. 11,850 for a thousand copies, each with 600 pages.

Indian Insect Pests was published under a Preface dated the 1st of May 1906.

On the back of the title page was a quotation from Eleanor Ormerod, dated the 25th of September 1885, at St Alban's:

But, meanwhile, I may most truly say that, if the crop of timber or fruit growers of India were furnished with plain and comprehensive accounts of history and habits of the common insect pests, accompanied by wood-cut figures, so as to convey the appearance of pests without wearisome description of details, all this would be a national benefit, repaying the outlay a hundred times.

The Preface, not from Mr Mollison but from Mr F.G. Sly, the officiating Inspector General, states that the book is intended to serve as a manual for the intelligent agriculturalist and also as a textbook in agricultural colleges and schools.

> Mr. Lefroy would prefer to postpone publication but I think the information is sufficiently important to give the public and the best way to fill gaps is to show need for further help. The book is testimony to the strenuous efforts in the last three years by Mr. Lefroy, the only Entomologist in the Department of Agriculture.

The book, in fact, answered the requirements of Eleanor Ormerod, except that the illustrations were not all in wood-cut. There were 346, some drawings, some photographs. There were recipes for various emulsions, descriptions of bags and nets, the materials were costed. The text was as lucid and uncomplicated as one might expect, the pests classified entomologically but also as Caterpillars, Beetles, Locusts and Hoppers, and Sucking Insects. There were sections on the specific pests of Cotton, for instance, of Rice and Wheat, of Cane, Maize and Sorghum, of Leguminous Crops (Pulses), of Vegetable and Fruit Crops. There were, finally, 318 pages.

Within its limits, the book was a great success. It reached mainly the European officials and planters, but also a great many schools and well-educated Indians. It was certainly translated into Bengali, Hindi, Telugu and Gujerati, most probably into other Indian languages as well. A newspaper cutting, dated from Simla on the 4th of October, informs us:

> In the prospectus of Mr. H.M. Lefroy's forthcoming book on *Indian Insect Pests*, which has already been communicated to the Press, it was stated that the price would be Rs. 3 a copy. It has now been found possible to reduce the price to Rs. 1.8 a copy. The book will be published by the Superintendent of Government Printing, India, Calcutta.

This was a reduction to half-price, there being sixteen annas in a rupee.

Three thousand nine hundred copies were printed and 2,849 were given away, to Government officers and to a few private individuals. By 1910, there were fewer than a hundred left in stock. In the words of a later Acting Inspector General of Agriculture: 'It served its purpose splendidly and removed pressing want of a textbook...I consider the sale of this very important work very satisfactory considering the early development of scientific agriculture in India.'

At least one copy arrived in England. Thanking him for a copy of his school's magazine, Harold's mother wrote, on the 4th of April 1907, to the headmaster of Church Hill House:

Dear Mr. Creed

Thank you for the 'Crondallian' which is very interesting and will I hope long continue in its present very attractive form. I send you a copy of my son's book hoping that as he is an 'old boy' you will give it a place in your school library. It is not too technical to interest boys who are fond of Natural History. It has been most favourably reviewed in the Indian Press & Government ordered 2,000 copies of it.

Yours sincerely

E.C. Maxwell Lefroy

P.S. Could you come to tea on Friday the 12th? I have asked some of the Cunninghams to come.

Nor was this the only publication of Harold's to arrive in Great Britain. On the 11th of June 1906, *The Times* remarked:

Mr. H. Maxwell-Lefroy's Memoirs of the *Dept. of Agriculture in India*, published in 1905, has arrived rather late but affords interesting reading upon the Bombay Locust, to which the Memoirs are exclusively directed. It is therefore a 'memoir of the Bombay Locust,' copiously illustrated with maps and plates showing the life history and methods of destruction. The effect of insecticides and the entire locust problem is discussed in an attractive and very instructive manner. The same post brought a copy of the *Quarterly Agricultural Journal of India*, containing reports on the renovation and deterioration of tea and orange cultivation, on the moth-borer in sugar-cane, maize and sorghum in western India.

On the 17th of May 1906, Harold was officially gazetted as Imperial Entomologist to the Government of India. No uncharted increase in salary followed this, but it was a rise in status.

The question of which vernacular language Harold was to learn must have been under discussion all this time, and it was now suggested that he should concentrate on Hindustani, with the expectation of being examined in it within the year, or two years at the outside.

Hindustani was about as close as any of the Indian languages came to being universal in India. Hindi was the form of Sanskritised Hindustani spoken by educated Hindus, while Urdu was a Persianised form spoken by educated Muslims. They were mutually intelligible to an extent, but below a relatively high educational level Hindustani was of no use. In order to communicate with the *ryot*, the true peasant farmers of India, their own language had to be used, and an interpreter was essential.

The next year opened with the marriage of Lucy O'Meara to Robert Steel Finlow. As he was later to become Fibre Expert (Jute) to the Bengal Government, and later still Director of Agriculture in Bengal, we must suppose that he was part of the Agricultural Establishment at Pusa. They seem to have become engaged in October 1906.

Anne Elizabeth, the eldest O'Meara sister, was married to Lawrence Lewton-Brain, a plant pathologist, whom she had met in Barbados. He had intended to become a doctor but found that he could not stand the operations. He decided to doctor plants instead and became Director of Agriculture in Malaya and the Federated Malay States. The Lewton-Brains were at this time in Honolulu where he had been invited by the Hawaiian Planters' Scientific Association to advise on diseases affecting their pineapple and cotton crops.

Very little is known of the childhood of the O'Meara sisters. Anne Elizabeth and Kathleen seem to have spent some time in a convent near Malines in Belgium, leaving the former with a lifelong dislike of *sauerkraut*. Lucy must have been living with the Maxwell-Lefroys since their marriage, as there was nowhere else for her to go. Their parents had died sufficiently recently for the distribution of their property still to be under discussion. Writing to Bob Finlow, to congratulate him on their approaching relationship, Anne Elizabeth said: 'Mr. Lefroy has interfered so much in the division, that he has annoyed and exasperated the trustees, that for a year we have not heard anything from them. We hope, however, to have everything settled shortly.' And slightly more ominously: 'I am afraid Lucy did not get on very well with Mr. Lefroy. He has an unfortunate manner, and lack of tact, which is rather trying...'

Kathleen wrote more cheerfully: '...and let me help you. Hal will be on the spot, so he can give you advice and no doubt *condolence*, which should be appropriated from his point of view, on any engagement.'

On the 24th of October, Bob Finlow wrote to Lucy: 'Just at present it looks as though you will have to risk Mr. Lefroy's displeasure if you marry me...Mr. Lefroy says we do not know each other well enough to marry.'

It seems that Lucy spent that winter in Honolulu, returning to Pusa to be married in February or March. Their son Gerald was born on the 17th of December 1907 and their marriage appears to have been perfectly happy. We may suppose that the bride was given away by her brother-in-law and we may also suppose that he did so with a very considerable sigh of relief.

Mrs Gabrielle Howard and Mr F.M. Howlett were to arrive at Pusa in this year. Mrs Howard was something new to the Government of India, a graduate of Newnham College, Cambridge. She had taken First Class Honours in the Natural Science Tripos in 1898. She was essentially a botanist, more specifically an economic botanist, but she had also a fluent knowledge of French and German, and a working knowledge of scientific Italian. She was married to Mr Albert Howard, the Economic Botanist at Pusa, and now applied for a post as his supernumerary. This, however, was refused on the ground that they might find themselves posted to completely different parts of India; there could be no guarantee of a second post if her husband were transferred.

Mr Howlett, appointed from the Indian Museum, was the Second Entomologist. It appears that he and Harold already knew one another. He was in England at the time of his appointment and, in February, requested permission to delay his arrival in Pusa until October, both on account of undisclosed private business and because Harold had asked him to work on some of the material he had sent back to the Natural History Museum in South Kensington.

He was also anxious to work up his extensive collection of *Diptera* – the blood-sucking insects – which he had brought with him to Britain and which he could not work on at Pusa because there were no facilities and because there was no literature.

'Maxwell-Lefroy has entrusted me with writing a proportion of a large work on Indian entomology which it is proposed to issue for the use of students and others.'

He also suggested that entomologists should be granted short periods of home leave every three or four years, to keep themselves in touch with developments in the rest of the world.

> Dr. Sharp, with whom I had conversation yesterday, is strongly of this opinion and from what Maxwell-Lefroy has told me he would raise no objection – to work 4 months at South Kensington and Cambridge in order to work on specimens brought back, also to make a special study of literature on the subject; I would work alongside Dr. Sharp during the long vacation.

This proposal was approved by the Viceroy, now Lord Minto.

Expansion at Pusa seems to have continued on all fronts in 1907. To deal with the vastly increased correspondence of the Imperial Mycologist and of the Imperial Entomologist a Superintendent, with three clerks and a typist, were taken on. Four new clerks joined the Accounts Department and a librarian was appointed, the new staff recruited at an annual cost of 4,800 rupees.

The appointment of a Third Entomologist, an expert in *Diptera*, was recommended, and that of two temporary assistants. There were by now more than fifty officers in the Indian Agriculture Service. There had only been six in 1901.

Harold's own budget was increased by 1000 rupees to pay for two more assistants who were to tour constantly. He was given an extra allowance of 240 rupees for 'dearness of food' and the temporary employment of a watchman, at six rupees a month, was sanctioned for his office. This was possibly because, in May 1906, his office had been broken into and more than 700 rupees stolen.

The accumulation of interest on the Phipps Donation, 106,000 rupees, was given to the Southern India Pasteur Institute. This was achieved a little ahead of a complaint from London that the buildings at Pusa, which were by no means complete, had already exceeded their estimates – by 3 *lakhs* and 49,714 rupees, in fact. A *lakh* was 100,000.

By the 7th of August what is still referred to as Harold's textbook is considered to be nearing completion. The Inspector General wrote, to the Government of India:

> The greater part is now ready for the press and the illustrations are nearly complete. Lefroy is a busy man and he doesn't want to spare more time on his book until he knows for certain that publication is sanctioned by Government. He can drop the work for six months if there is no prospect of immediate sanction. I strongly recommend that it should be published without delay.

The cost of a thousand copies is estimated at 12,000 rupees and, as there was little chance of such a sum being saved from the agricultural budget, the Inspector General respectfully recommended that the Government should pay.

The ravages of the Bollworm, particularly in the Punjab, had by now been brought almost under control. Bollworms are the larvae of small, buff-coloured moths called *Earias insulana* and *Earias fabia*. They feed only on the shoots and seeds of members of the Mallow family, the *Malvaceae*, which includes Hollyhocks, Abutilons, the Hibiscuses and, in particular, okra or *bhindi*, *Hibiscus esculentus*, and cotton plants, *Gossypium* of various kinds. 'The habit of the larvae of boring into shoots and seed pods is unusual and notable for members of this group.'

Bhindi had been planted as a 'trap crop', that is to say it was planted alongside the cotton, or all round it, in the hope that the Bollworm would eat the *bhindi* rather than the cotton. But the most effective method of control had proved to be the introduction of the Bollworm's natural enemy, a very small black ichneumon fly, *Rhogas*

Lefroyi, and this was by now established in most of the important cotton-growing areas.

Gelechia Gossypiella, 'the notorious pink boll worm of India, Ceylon, Burmah, Straits Settlements and East Africa', also had a natural parasite, *Apanteles depressariae*, which, in Harold's words, 'commonly pupate in very noticeable white cocoons, openly on the plant near their victim or on it', This too, had been successfully introduced. The cotton-growers of India, however, were proving very reluctant to try different kinds of cotton plant.

Attacks of the Potato Moth, *Phthorimaea operculella* or *Lita solanella*, had been similarly brought under control. Imported from Italy in a cargo of seed potatoes, it had done enormous damage over the past years. By storing the seed potatoes dry in sand during the monsoon, and planting them out in October, the problem was solved; but it was to be several years before this method became widely adopted.

It is clear that Harold's attention at this time was much occupied by the antics of the Wheat Weevil, which could also be largely controlled by providing storage conditions adverse to it. He considered that an expert was required to devote his whole time to it and, until such a person had reported fully, that it was unwise to make any statement. What is described as a 'surface caterpillar' on tobacco is also under investigation. It requires only care to control it, no poisons or special appliances; but 'only the *ryot's* aversion to taking life prevents him from treating in a commonsense way.'

The infestation of imported plant materials was by now a matter of urgent concern. In a report of the 25th of June Harold wrote:

> Insects known to have been introduced:
>   The following cases have come to my personal knowledge since I arrived in India.
>   (a) Pulse seeds imported from a good European firm, destroyed by the Pea-beetle, which was still alive when the parcel was opened.
>   (b) Another case of the same kind, the seed imported from Calcutta.

(c) Maize seeds of a specially good variety – infested with the Rice Weevil.

(d) Flax seeds infested with caterpillars.

(e) A consignment of specially good pines from the West Indies – covered with Scale Insects.

(f) Yams, also from the West Indies. Scale Insects.

These are insects imported in the living state, probably occurring continually.

I have a list of 213 insects known to be injurious to Indian agriculture, of these probably 3 were directly introduced; the Sweet Potato Weevil (though some entomologists believe this originated in India): the Diamond Back Moth of cabbage and the Potato Moth. Out of a total of 8 aphides six were probably introduced. 12 moths occur not only in India but all over the world.

A list of these moths followed, and a list of thirty insects destructive to grain. Considering the enormous size of the problem and the almost complete unawareness of it on the part of non-entomologists, he was making significant strides.

Every plant can be fumigated with hydrocyanic acid provided the leaves are not wet. The point is to make fumigation automatic whether an import has insects or not. I would accept the principle accepted by the Governments of the West Indies, that imports of fruit and vegetables for consumption should be left alone; but plants, bulbs, tubers etc. should be fumigated.

Experiments with fumigation were being carried out at Pusa, to find the strength required to kill the eggs of Scale Insects; the maximum strength that will not injure living plants, cuttings or bulbs in any way; and the strength required to destroy all insects, and their eggs, without damaging the plants.

Twenty *lakhs* of rupees had already been spent on Pusa. Although they were not officially open, they were accepting students and hoped to open formally in October of that year. But, with all this activity, with the gradually increasing success of his methods in controlling the insect pests, the most important event of 1907 must have been the birth of a second healthy son, Cecil Anthony, on the 7th of July.

CHAPTER VIII

Harold had by now four Indian Assistants in the laboratory at Pusa and, on the 28th of October, the Inspector General, at Harold's instigation, wrote to the Government of India on the subject of raising their pay. 'Their services can only be retained if their pay is increased.'

Mr S.C. Misra was on 200 rupees a month, rising gradually to a maximum of 250. He had received his practical training at Nagpur Agricultural College, in the Central Provinces, and had been an Assistant Master at the Rajkumar College. A man of extremely practical mind, he had been given the task of teaching elementary entomology, 'which he does in a very thorough manner. From a good Cawnpore family, his influence on both students and staff is excellent. It is extremely necessary to retain his services as First Assistant.' An immediate rise of 50 rupees is asked for here, increasing to 400 a month.

Mr C.C. Ghosh, the Second Assistant, was a graduate of Calcutta University, his degree in biology including both botany and physics. In charge of the Insectary at Pusa, he had done difficult and excellent work and his pay should be doubled, from 75 rupees a month to 150, rising to 300.

Mr Gobindram Dutt, the Third Assistant, had his BA from Punjab University. He is mentioned as being of particularly good family and

66

it is recommended that he be trained to succeed the First Assistant, should it prove impossible to retain Mr Misra. His pay should be similarly doubled, rising to 250 rupees a month.

The Fourth Assistant, Mr D. Nowroji, had a BA from Madras University, with zoology as his special subject, and a rise is asked for similar to Mr Dutt's.

To these requests is added the statement that, while a very high standard of training is required, a university degree is not essential. The rates of pay proposed are more or less on a level with those appropriate to superintendents on Government farms. While it will be desirable that all men trained in England should be appointed to responsible posts under the Economic Botanist in the Provinces, such men cannot be available for a number of years. The highest rate of pay, 300 rupees rising to 600, is therefore not proposed for the Entomology Assistants at Pusa at present.

These requests were accepted by Government and went into effect in February of the next year, Mr Misra finally achieving 400 rupees a month and the others 300.

On the 25th of November, Mr F.M. Howlett, now the Second Imperial Entomologist, sailed for India. He was to be paid 600 rupees a month, rising to an eventual 1,000. As his journey is mentioned in the official documents – he was to proceed to Waini Station on the Tirhoot State Railway – it is fair to assume that he had never been to Pusa before. He was to have a particularly friendly and fruitful relationship with Harold and his arrival must have been especially welcome.

The next year opened with a sharp note from the Public Works Department, Bengal, to the Public Works Department, India, demanding to know who, at Pusa, was required to pay rent. It was replied that some people were exempt by virtue of their agreements but that, for instance, Harold Maxwell-Lefroy, in No. 2 European Quarters, should pay rent in accordance with the PWD Code.

In February the British Cotton Growing Association withdrew its grant of £10,000 to India, not because of their inability to control cotton pests, but because they refused to experiment with new kinds of cotton plant.

In February, too, Dr Leather, the Imperial Agricultural Chemist, complained to Government that he had been obliged to insert into his training programme certain work which he knew to be useless. To which Government briskly replied, not to Dr Leather but to the Inspector General, that Dr Leather was not entitled to address them directly. He should have done so through the Inspector General who, in future, was to endorse all programmes decided on by the Board of Agriculture.

Everything had to be requested through the proper channels, indented for and the appropriate requisitions issued, and this applied to Harold as much as to everyone else. Only in the field can he really be considered as a free agent. At the beginning of March 1908, for instance, he put in a request for a special grant of 25,000 rupees for the purchase of microscopes, micro-apparatus, dissecting instruments and various kinds of laboratory apparatus for the use of his students. At the end of the month, Government replied that they could not sanction a grant of this size in the current financial year, but they would nevertheless authorise direct purchase from the manufacturers of all essential equipment. 'As it is extremely important that research work should start as soon as possible, all urgently required apparatus can be set against the Supplies and Service Budget for 1908–1909.'

The Examination in the Vernacular now loomed. In March the Inspector General asked where the examination should take place and, in May, was told that Bankipore – site of the Great Granary, built in 1780 – suitably near Pusa, was appropriate. They were required to translate a passage from a newspaper; to read from a book or textbook; and to hold a conversation at village level, about cattle, land or crops.

But all the emphasis now moved towards the Research Institute itself and at the end of April a Provisional Prospectus was produced. Provided that the laboratories were equipped in time, the Institute expected to open on the 1st of July, giving specialised post-graduate courses to selected students.

Pusa is described as being situated in the district of Darbhanga, Bengal, six miles from the station of Waini on the Bengal and North West Railway. The main building, the two-storied Phipps Laboratory, has well-equipped laboratories for each branch of agricultural sciences, a library and a reading room, a museum, lecture halls, a drawing office and a photographic dark room. The building is fitted with electric light and fans, and gas and water are laid on. There are quarters for European and Indian staff, and a large hostel with accommodation for seventy students. There are recreation grounds and a well-equipped hospital and dispensary for both staff and students, with a qualified medical officer.

A farm of 400 acres has buildings for all experiments and instruction, including Pot Culture. There is an Insectary. Another 400 acres have been set aside for cattle-breeding and dairy supply. Seventy-five acres have been laid out as a botanical garden and there is a botanical laboratory.

It is a description of a very pleasant place. Small wonder, then, that the staff now assembled there should have been so enthusiastic about the establishment that was emerging from the welter of correspondence, from the committee meetings, and from the discussions, amiable and otherwise, as to what should be taught there.

The staff is described as a Principal, with the Imperial Agricultural Chemist, the Imperial Mycologist, Entomologist, Economic Botanist, Agriculturalist, Agricultural Bacteriologist and the 2nd Imperial Entomologist; in other words – all the top people in their field in India.

They were offering two-year courses in one only of the following: Agricultural Chemistry, Economic Botany, Economic Entomology, Mycology and Agricultural Bacteriology, though the latter was not yet available.

The students' expenses were expected to be in the region of 25 rupees a month, with books and stationery on top of that. They had to make their own arrangements about food, each caste and religion having its own cook room and dining quarters. Married students had to leave their wives and children behind, and dogs were not allowed in the College precincts, an essential precaution against rabies. Horses and cows could only be kept with the permission of the Principal. There were to be three classes of student, those nominated by a local government or administration, those deputed by a native state and those paying their own expenses, although these were not admitted to start with.

There were of course dissensions and complaints. Harold suggested that Zoology, recommended by a sub-committee, was unnecessary, being of no value to agricultural students. Mr Howlett supported him, but the Principal of the Poona Agricultural College considered it should be included as some students 'scarcely know the difference between bone and muscle'. Later the Government of Bombay was to complain that the Pusa prospectus differed very little from that of the Poona Agricultural College. 'Unless Pusa can offer instruction to continue and develop the work of the Provincial Colleges, it will not justify its existence.' The discussions continued.

Meanwhile, until these excellent arrangements could be completed, the conditions for those on the spot left something to be desired. Mr S.C. Misra, in particular, stated that he had been promised rent-free accommodation, but this had not been forthcoming. The quarters allocated to him had been unsuitable. Harold supported him: 'I understood that all Assistants would have rent-free accommodation. Mr. Misra was compelled to remove his family for proper medical attention. One child died, another was ill for a long time. It would be wise to provide proper medical attention before an epidemic drives out our staff and stops work.'

Mr Misra was also having to pay a teacher for his children, 18 rupees a month, as there were no good schools. There are complaints at this time that the cost of living at Pusa was very high. Before the end of the year, however, Mr Misra was provided with rent-free housing – though this privilege was not extended to his successor – and a First Class Hospital Assistant was engaged.

A correspondence now arose about the courses available to any students at Pusa who qualified for further instruction. This followed a letter in the previous December, from the Secretary to the Government of India, saying that a halt should be called in the number of Europeans working at Pusa. 'Very strong justification would be required before any proposals to employ further experts from England could be entertained.'

The proposal for a student of Entomology was that he should take a degree course at Cambridge, followed by a course of practical work away from laboratories and lectures. There were, at that time – and this is surprising – no facilities for courses of that sort in England, but they were available in Europe. There would be a language problem there, but this would not be the case in the United States, at either Amherst or Massachusetts. Practical courses were regarded as essential to enable the student to bring his scientific knowledge to bear on the ordinary problems of agriculture.

Both the Imperial Mycologist and the Imperial Entomologist now wished to expand their departments, and their wishes were endorsed by the Inspector General.

> It is unnecessary for me to refer pointedly to the work already accomplished by Dr E.J. Butler and Mr Maxwell-Lefroy in India. It has been very prolific in research and publications, and most valuable in practical application. We have in these two officers extremely able and enthusiastic workers. In their respective line of work I am certain that no more able men are employed in any part of the world.

The list of Harold's publications, attached to this Memorandum, of his Leaflets, Bulletins and Memoirs, is a long one. It includes leaflets on *Methods of destroying Locust Hoppers* (translated into three north Indian languages), on *Insects attacking Cotton* (translated into two north and one south Indian language) and on *The Moth-borer in Sugar-cane* (into two north Indian languages). There were leaflets on the uses of Kerosene Emulsion, Crude Oil Emulsion, Lead Arsenate and on Rosin Washes; on the Dusky Cotton Bug, the Red Cotton Bug, the Cotton Leaf Hopper and the Six-Spotted Ladybird Beetle.

Simple spraying apparatuses are described in two leaflets and there is a summary of the lectures on entomology which he had given at the Poona Agricultural College.

By the end of the year, he had published memoirs on the Mustard Sawfly, the Rice Bug, the Red Cotton Bug, the Castor Semi-looper, the Tobacco Caterpillar and the Cotton Leaf Roller. There were articles in the *Agricultural Journal of India*: 'Pests of Introduced Cotton', 'The Tsetse Fly in India', 'The Tobacco Stem-borer', 'The Sugar-cane Borers of Behar' and 'Insect Pests of the Mangel Wurzel'. Two articles, 'Practical Remedies for Insect Pests' and 'Imported Insect Pests' were of particular importance at that time; and this was all in addition to the book on *Indian Insect Pests*, already published, and the one on Indian insect life on which he was still working.

The cultivation of silk continued at Pusa. The rearing of the Lac Insect, *Tachardia lacca*, was now the subject of experiment. This insect was used in the manufacture of both lacquer and shellac and was beginning to gain in importance with the increasing demand for gramophone records. Mr Howlett had taken over all the work on the 'biting flies', the *Diptera*, and a Mr Antram, Entomologist to the Indian Tea Association, continued his investigations into insects injurious to the tea plant.

On the 17th of October 1908, Harold accepted permanent employment with the Government of India. The Inspector General recommended that this be back-dated to the 30th of April and this was agreed in February of the following year.

This was the year of the incident then known as the Muzaffarpur Outrage. Two young Bengalis arrived in Muzaffarpur with the intention of murdering Mr Kingsford, the District Judge, who, as Chief Presidency Magistrate of Calcutta, had ordered the flogging of a number of young Bengalis for singing a Nationalist song. This had been regarded as seditious. They threw their bombs, but into the wrong carriage, killing the wife and daughter of a local collector who had had nothing whatever to do with the case.

One of the boys shot himself dead. The other, aged nineteen, was caught, tried and hanged.

It caused a sensation all over Bengal and Bihar and must, in particular, have sent shock waves through Pusa, only thirty miles away.

The devotion, even the dedication, of the European staff to their work can never for a moment be doubted. Their quiet determination, in the words of the future Sir Albert Howard, 'to improve Indian agriculture on its own lines', was in the end to prove one of the most lasting of the British legacies to India. Their well-intentioned, and largely successful, efforts to increase the national food supply, by increasing the yield of their cash crops, and therefore to benefit the greatest possible number of people – even if they did refer to them as 'natives' – must have been a source of permanent satisfaction to them and to their students. An event of this kind can only have caused them all a great deal of distress.

Inevitably, in these early days, there were frictions at Pusa. In February 1909, the Mycology First Assistant resigned and gave as his reasons: that Indian Assistants with high educational qualifications were not called Assistant Professors, but Assistant Teachers; that they were not permitted to borrow books from the library; that the garden area and some other public areas were closed to members of the subordinate staff, who were also not allowed to keep horses or dogs; that relations between the European officers and their Indian subordinates were 'strained'; and that the subordinate staff were not allowed to seek employment in other departments except under penalty of dismissal.

The Inspector General asked the Director at Pusa if he would put all these matters right.

Harold, however, seems to have remained on good terms with his Assistants. He once again corresponded with Government, through the Inspector General, about increases in their pay. Mr Ghosh, in particular, has continued to do excellent work. He is in direct charge of the Insectary and is highly skilled in the rearing of insects of all kinds. He is also in charge of the Silk Worm House and the cultivation of Eri silk at Pusa. It is his work which has made all these things so successful and, although this is not precisely stated, it is clear that Harold is afraid of losing him to a higher appointment in a provincial department. The other two, Mr Dutt and Mr Nowroji, are both excellent men whom he is anxious to keep with him, and he therefore has the honour to suggest pay rises for them all.

On the other side, a European supernumerary Entomologist, whose three-year appointment was due to end in more than a year's time, seems to have been giving rather less than satisfaction. From Harold's report on him:

> The impression I have is that he is unable to grasp *together* the nature of experiments to be made, the facts to be deduced and conclusions to be drawn. So there is a mass of disconnected work which leads nowhere. He carries out work but cannot deduce facts, or modify his work accordingly. Few men can. In 1908 he visited the Central Province and Assam, to investigate the potato moth and outbreaks of pests in rice. His reports were of value, though nothing could be done to check them. In the same year he toured Army Store depots to check on damage done by a beetle. The work was good and thorough, and suffers only from his inability to write a report and express himself satisfactorily. He arranged show cases for the Muzarffarpur Exhibition, took a great deal of trouble and did very good work. He was specially trained for it at Wye. His work is characterised by a marked want of initiative. He takes opportunities thrust upon him but doesn't make them. It is extremely thorough work but as a rule leads nowhere. When it is a question of routine work there is less difficulty. I am unable to leave answering letters to him. In a routine post his work would not matter. When scientific enquiry is required it is all important. I am uncertain if he has the ability for a Provincial Entomologist...I have encouraged him in every way to do independent work. He has been urged to make a distinct line of his own...He has had every possible opportunity but has not made much of them.

Forwarding the report to Government, the Inspector General remarked: 'Lefroy is a very ardent worker himself. He expects perhaps more than is possible from some of his assistants.'

In fact, it is the owner of a highly original, questing mind commenting on the owner of an unoriginal, routine mind which, however fully he may have understood it, he could not bring himself to admire. Now that he had had ample time to understand completely the size and complexity of the various problems raised by the activities of insects in India, it is possible that Harold felt that his progress would have been even swifter had he had an assistant who could have assisted him rather than one whom he apparently had to assist.

In March of the following year, the Inspector General recommended that both Harold and Dr Butler should be excused the vernacular examination. Both had sufficient knowledge of Hindi to make themselves understood, and to understand. Their work had not in any way suffered from the fact that neither had complete knowledge of any one Indian language. Preparation for the examination would seriously interrupt their other work.

The recommendation was accepted, and in May they were officially excused, no doubt to the great relief of them both.

CHAPTER IX

Harold now returned to the problem of preventing the importation of insect pests on plants from other countries, one of the things he felt most deeply about. In June of the previous year, the Director of Agriculture, Bombay, had supplied full details of the imports of fruit, vegetables, living plants, tubers and seeds, their quantities, their sources and their destinations. Now, in May 1909, Harold issued a report with the Director of the Agricultural College at Pusa.

It suggested that Sir Daniel Morris, now Agricultural Adviser to the Colonial Office, should be asked to acknowledge the necessity for other colonies, in Africa for instance, or the Further East, to keep India informed about their agricultural insect pests. India was not a colony. It was a self-sufficient Empire and its administration was entirely separate from that of the Colonial Office. Nevertheless: 'Entomologists in some British colonies make demands on this Department for assistance in connection with a supply of parasitic insects to check their pests.'

It is probable that the information now available at Pusa on all aspects of tropical and sub-tropical agriculture was the most up-to-date of any in the British Empire at that time.

Among the information received from Bombay, the largest port in India, was a suggestion that arrangements should be made to exclude all possible pests of tea, coffee, rubber and fruit; anything that threatened the staple annual crops; and anything that could injure all forms of vegetation, roadside trees, for instance, and ordinary garden plants.

The report remarks that the last of these is not necessary; but the main aims must be to exclude anything of danger to the annual crops and to protect the perennial ones. There are comments on various imports, which have already been considered.

The action required is specific.

(1) Details of every import are to be recorded at the port of entry.
(2) If the Imperial Entomologist considers an import to be dangerous, he shall recommend to Government the necessary steps to be taken.
(3) The fumigation of *all* living plants, and parts of plants, should take place at the port of entry.
(4) This applies to articles sent by post as well as those arriving by sea.
(5) The sample form of the schedule of imports has been prepared.
(6) List enclosed of dangerous plants only to be allowed in after fumigation: tea, coffee, rubber, citrus of all kinds, mango, litchi, date, apples, pear, plum, peach, guava, apricot, grape vine, palms, figs, pomegranates, indigo and cotton.

Very detailed facts and figures are given of various experiments carried out at Pusa and the establishment of a fumigating house at all ports of entry is recommended, its dimensions also being specified. Each one of these recommendations was to be accepted. In September of the following year, the Government of India circulated an instruction pamphlet containing them to all the Provincial Governments.

The Prospectus for the Agricultural Research Institute and College was now issued, not so very different from the Provisional Prospectus of the previous year.

It is now recognised that the first and most essential condition of any permanent improvement in agricultural methods of this country is the widest possible diffusion of an organised knowledge of science and practical agriculture, and at the same time it is desired to make the country as far as possible self-supporting in the matter of the development of agricultural training and research. A comprehensive scheme for the promotion of agricultural education throughout India has accordingly been drawn up as the result of which it is hoped that every important province will soon be provided with a fully equipped college where students will for three years receive practical and scientific education in agriculture. The position which the Pusa College is intended to occupy is that of a higher teaching institution. Its main object is to enable students who have passed with distinction through a course of a provincial college, by means of a post-graduate course in one of the specialised branches of agricultural science, to qualify for the higher branches of agricultural work.

Of the syllabus it says: 'In the absence of experience in the class of student likely to be received, it is impossible to lay down a permanent syllabus of training of each subject. The following syllabus is tentative, but time will not be wasted in taking students over ground familiar to them.'

This indicates a degree of open-mindedness not altogether common at that time. One must hope that the teaching was conducted in a comparably relaxed fashion. Certainly they cannot have known what to expect from their students, coming from schools and colleges all over India, described in the Prospectus as being 'of very unequal merit'; but the College appears to have been a success from the start, its students making full use of their new knowledge and transforming the agriculture of their country. 'Students nominated should ordinarily be men who have passed with credit through a provincial agricultural college or are graduates of an Indian University, or possess a degree or diploma.' They should be aged not less than nineteen.

The Entomology course was for one year.

1. Collecting, pinning, setting
2. How to use textbooks, collections
3. Anatomy of cockroach or other form. Comparative anatomy as shown by dissection. Terms used in classifying
4. Classification and terms used in each order
5. Actual identification and revision of collection
6. Biology and life histories – general, special and details
7. An account of each family in order
8. Pests: General, then special by order, then special by crop

9. Comprehensive list of injurious pests of India
10. Preparation of leaflets and lecture course for a Province, with exhibits and collections
11. Useful insects (lac, silk, apiculture)
12. Beneficial birds and insects
13. Preventive and remedial measures

The Autumn Term was to run from the 1st of June to the 15th of November, and the Spring Term from the 6th of January to the 31st of March. The College seems to have been run on lines very similar to those of a residential college in Britain. Misdemeanours were punished by an entry in the Conduct Register, by a stoppage of leave or a fine, or by removal and dismissal from College, depending on their nature and their seriousness.

But, for Harold, the principal event of 1909 must have been the publication of his book, *Indian Insect Life*.

It is described as:

A Manual of the Insects of the Plains (Tropical India)
by H. Maxwell-Lefroy, M.A., F.E.S., F.Z.S.
Entomologist, Imperial Department of Agriculture for India; Author of 'Indian Insect Pests', etc.

Assisted by
F.M. Howlett, B.A., F.E.S.
Second Entomologist, Imperial Department of Agriculture for India.

Published under the Authority of the Government of India
Agricultural Research Institute, Pusa

Calcutta and Simla, Thacker, Spink and Co.
W. Thacker & Co., 2 Creed Lane, London
1909

Dedicated only 'To My Mother' – his father had died in the previous year – it carried on the other side of the dedication page the following, unattributed comment:

Plus je connais les peoples,
Plus j'aime les insects.

This could perhaps be loosely translated as:

The more I know of people
The more I care for bugs.

There were 84 coloured plates and 536 line drawings or photographs in black and white. With the index, there were 786 pages.

There was a characteristically modest page of Acknowledgements.

Where not otherwise acknowledged, all the plates and illustrations are the work of the Artist staff of this Institute under my or Mr. Howlett's direction; it may be pointed out that these artists are wholly Natives of India, trained in Art Schools of this country; it is needless to emphasize how much the book owes to their beautiful work as also to the enterprise of the publishers, who have done the work of reproducing all the illustrations in this country.

The volume is largely a product of my spare time and scanty holidays; such a volume has been so much required that I have felt that even an imperfect one was better than none.

I may also emphasise the fact that where little is said, little is known and the blanks in the book are designedly prominent to emphasise the enormous scope there is for work.

I trust also that the volume may be a real stepping-stone to better things and may help those who are advancing our knowledge of the insect life of India.

From the Introduction:

Insects are of all sizes from one fiftieth of an inch long to over six inches; their numbers are incalculable, the number of their species being put at about three millions; their lives are very short, (a week,) up to as long as over ten years, though rarely exceeding more than three years, and being in the larger number limited to an active life of less than three months.

What is the life of an insect? In what way can it be compared with our own or with the life, for instance, of any of the animals familiar to us? No answer can easily be given, for the senses, the instincts, the modes of expression of insects are so totally diverse from our own that there is scarcely any point of contact.

In the case of mammals, of birds and to some extent reptiles, we have in the eyes, in the features and in the movements, a clue to their feelings, to the emotions that sway them, to the motives that guide their actions; in insects we have none, and the great index of insect feeling, the antenna, has no counterpart in higher minds and conveys nothing to our uninformed brains.

We can judge then only from the movements of insects, from their actions, and this is so extraordinarily meagre a clue that it is not surprising that even the greatest familiarity with the life of an insect inspires no feeling that one has to do with a live organism having feelings and passions, having motives and a will, but suggests that one has before one a beautiful machine, tuned to respond mechanically to certain outside stimuli, to answer to particular influences and to behave in all things as a perfect mechanical structure.

…one comes inevitably to the feeling that insects are a supreme expression of living matter adapted and co-ordinated to physical conditions, responding perfectly to mechanical stimuli, without mind or mental processes as we know them and as we can see them in birds and mammals; they are the highest expression of life as evolved by natural processes, perfect machines without emotions.

Insects have lived, have dominated the earth, have become what we see them by carrying to an extreme the principle of adaptation to circumstances, of making the most of natural conditions; man has become what he is, because he has carried to an extreme the principle of adapting natural conditions to himself while only adapting himself to them to a limited extent; the two classes dominate the land, and when men cannot alter the conditions to make life permanently bearable, insects can adapt themselves and do. But in the process man has developed one form of mentality implied in the terms free-will, choice, volition, while insects have become perfect mechanical structures reacting in a definite way to natural forces and stimuli, their lives ruled by fixed and most perfect 'instincts'.

A section then followed for each Order of Insects.

APTERA The order includes only a small number of minute wingless insects of extreme delicacy, supposed to be scavengers.

ORTHOPTERA The order is divided into seven clearly defined families, four of which form one series in which the hind legs are normal, three of which form a second series in which the hind legs are long and formed for leaping.

Locusts and grasshoppers are included here.

Insects are small creatures and very abundant; where are they all? At some times in the year one can easily gather at least one hundred thousand insects within one day over a space of, say, a few acres; at another time there would not appear to be an insect obtainable in that space and yet the insects must be somewhere.

NEUROPTERA The order includes predaceous and scavenging, land and aquatic insects. None are parasitic, and none herbivorous.

Bird lice, book lice and termites come in this section.

…we find that the great mass of insects are, as far as we know, wholly solitary. Consider the commonest insects there are about us, and watch their ways; all live for themselves individually and appear to take no notice of each other, except when impelled by the mating instinct. It is perhaps safe to say 'apparently' because for all we know there may be modes of inter-communication not revealed by external movements, as there must certainly be in some species of ants.

HYMENOPTERA The sawflies, gallflies, ichneumons, cuckoo-wasps, bees, ants and wasps which make up this order are readily recognised in the field: the order is a very large one, with a greater number of known species, and perhaps a greater number of undescribed species than any order except *Diptera*.

Possibly insects are dominant because they are small, reproduction can be quick and vast, an egg can contain enough food to produce an active self-supporting larva; the difficulties of viviparism (giving birth to live young) are avoided and the mother need not live over to care for her young. When the seasons are unfavourable, the female waits with her store of undeveloped eggs till the season is favourable.

COLEOPTERA (Beetles) The order includes minute to large insects, of varied habits, including herbivores, predators, scavengers, both aquatic and terrestrial, with no social and scarcely any parasitic forms.

It is a matter of daily observation that many birds and some mammals find that insects are an excellent food and one may wonder that man has not found this also. But in nothing are the vagaries and caprices of men better shown than in what he will and will not eat, and so a very large supply of food has, and apparently will, daily perish…Mankind eats many curious things, including oysters, shrimps, whelks and cockles, dried sea slugs (Holothurians), and birds' nests; the most civilised nation is addicted to eating snails, even uncooked; and yet there is an absurd prejudice against insects, not universal, but certainly covering the more civilised portions of mankind.

LEPIDOPTERA (Butterflies and Moths) The *imago* obtains its food from flowers or plant sap, the larva is herbivorous on or in plants, very rarely predaceous. In a large number the imaginal life is brief and no food is taken; in others it is longer; in all, the larval life is comparatively long and active.

Very little attention has been paid to that one moment in the lives of so many insects when the imago emerges from the pupa and has to make its way out of the cocoon or other pupal envelope. If the cocoon or covering is sufficiently perfect to resist the weather and the foes of the pupa, how is the usually soft and delicate insect to escape?...In a great number of species, especially the *Coleoptera*, the imago employs its own jaws...In many weevils the true mandibles are provided with false mandibles for this purpose, which drop off and leave a scar, after they have been used.

THYSANOPTERA (Thrips) Very little is known of thrips in India, though they occur commonly. We have two species which are destructive to pulse crops, but they have been found only once. Another is known to attack opium, a fourth is recorded as attacking turmeric in Madras...Others have recently been destructive to tea in Darjeeling...Specimens should be preserved in spirit, as they are useless dry, unless exceptionally large.

DIPTERA (Flies) by F.M. Howlett. The mosquitoes found in houses are mainly nocturnal in their habits, and may often be seen in the early morning trooping into the house in search of dark corners where they can shelter themselves from the light until evening. Lefroy's mosquito-trap takes advantage of this habit by providing a convenient dark box for the mosquitoes to rest in: when they have settled down for the day the box is closed and a few drops of benzene or chloroform introduced through a cork-hole in the top. The dead insects are afterwards removed and the box left open till next day.

RHYNCHOTA (Hemiptera) – Bugs. A large proportion of the sounds heard in the field are produced by insects and, while the motive that induces sound production is not always known, it is probably connected with sex, with simple forms of signalling and alarm giving, with protection from enemies, and finally with the simple expression of the emotions. The majority of the sounds heard are connected with sex, but it is by no means clear to what motive to attribute the loud continuous song of the Cicada, the most prominent of all insect noises.

An index of plants followed, with Latin, English and vernacular names, and a General Index followed that, insect names in Latin only.

The book was very well received, in the outside world as well as in India. In February 1910 a review appeared in the *Entomology News* of Philadelphia, under the initials H.S., thought to be those of Dr Harry Skinner, then President of the Entomological Society of America.

> ...and a valuable addition to the papers on Economic Entomology in India. It will have a stimulating effect not only on the study of species in the country, but in other tropical lands. The plates and figures appear to be excellent and accurate and the subject matter well written...A wonderful foundation has been laid and this foundation will undoubtedly be a great stimulus to bringing about future work...The authors are to be commended and congratulated on the production of this valuable and epoch-making volume. Now that Economic Entomology is being taken up the world over we hope to see similar works from some of the other tropical countries that have official entomologists.

The Entomologists' Record and Journal of Variation, of London, called it 'a tremendous book'. 'We are not surprised Mr. Maxwell Lefroy is proud of his Hindoo artists. They are well ahead of the best colour printers that try to illustrate our entomology work in Britain.'

It would be hard to find a tradition of painting more suited to insect illustration than the Indian one of that time, with its emphasis on meticulous accuracy, patient devotion to detail, purity of line and brilliance of colour. Each illustration was a work of art in its own right. The Hindoo artists appear to have worked on Harold's verandah, as an infant observer recorded:

> I believe I was once found eating paint on the verandah. That was where the artists worked. Yellow and green. I must have been about two at the time. And on another occasion I was found chewing some of my father's

cheroots in the sitting-room. I expect I found them very delicious. But I don't really remember this. I just remember being told.

On the 14th of September, Harold wrote to the Director at Pusa. Of *Indian Insect Pests* he said:

> …The influence of the book has been very marked and it has appealed to a wide audience, apparently because of its simple style and plain language. It has also put economic entomology on a higher plane altogether, and its educative effect is abundantly clear form the letters I receive. I do not think it is an exaggeration to say that the book is the equal of the best book in its class in other countries, and that the effect in India has been very far-reaching. Its sole defect is that it is in English and this is being remedied by translations.

With *Indian Insect Life*:

> Both books have been written almost entirely in my leisure time, between 6 and 8 p.m. I have had six weeks in the hills to finish it, but even then had my current work and a special investigation in hand. That this amount of writing has not interfered with my other work is shown by the volume of my contributions to the *Journal* and *Memoirs*. The illustrations, which are so important a feature, are in every sense my work. The artist staff were trained and made by me, up to 1908. The printing processes used I arranged for in connection with our *Journal* in 1905, and the 3-colour printing process is wholly due to my arrangement with our publishers and was done solely because I arranged for it, and guaranteed the work. The get-up and printing I have done personally myself, the whole of proof-correcting, etc. and the whole business of getting out the book not having occupied any part of my work hours or been done by any of my staff.
>
> The copyright of both books is the property of the Government and I have no prospect of benefiting pecuniarily from either. The above constitutes my justification for hoping that I may receive an honorarium for this work.   .

The honorarium was to be shared with Mr Howlett.

It was the beginning of a long correspondence, a correspondence that one feels should not have been necessary, that must have been slightly humiliating to conduct. It was not the first case of its kind; the honorarium could have been offered. In June 1904 Mr J.W. Mollison had received an honorarium of 1,500 rupees for his *Text Book on Indian Agriculture* but that may also have been the result of a similar correspondence. Harold's letter began its tedious journey through the usual channels.

The 'six weeks in the hills' – the only kind of 'scanty holiday' ever referred to in the official archives – are thought to have been spent in Mussoorie. It lay at the other end of the Siwalik Hills from Simla, less fashionable and less expensive, slightly lower, 6,600 feet, and in the opinion of many, more beautiful. It had a view to the south to the plains, and one to the north, to the everlasting snows; it had several schools of various denominations and, perhaps most important of all, it had a Roman Catholic Cathedral.

CHAPTER X

In November 1909 Mr Bernard Coventry went on leave.
He had first come to India, as an indigo planter, in 1881 and
had been Director and Principal of the Research Institute ever since it
started. Much of the credit for the fact that the Pusa Institute got so
quickly into its stride must be his. Virtually all the practical decisions
about the siting of buildings and the actual running of the College and
the Institute must have been made by him. He was later to become the
first Agricultural Advisor to the Government of India. Now, we may
suppose, he decided that the Institute was on a sufficiently sound basis
for him to absent himself for a few months without harm. Harold was
appointed Officiating Director while he was away.

The usual correspondence followed, between Inspector General
and Government, about whether increased responsibility merited an
increase in pay or not and, as a result, Harold was given an extra 250
rupees a month. That was in January. In March the Imperial Economic
Botanist entered the lists for a larger salary, one that was at least equal
to that of the Imperial Entomologist.

Without fully understanding conditions in India, Mr Howard,
engaged in Britain, had accepted a salary of 600 rupees a month,
rising to 800. The Imperial Entomologist had started at 750. The
Inspector General took up his case, and that of his wife, who had been

working as an unpaid assistant to her husband for five years. A salary of 400 rupees was finally agreed for her. 'We recognise that in ordinary circumstances the appointment of a lady to a regular appointment in the Indian Agricultural Service might form an undesirable precedent, but Mrs. Howard's case is so exceptional that we do not think the precedent can give rise to any trouble.'

Mrs Howard later became the Second Imperial Botanist, her husband being the First. They worked very smoothly together, spending eighteen years at Pusa. Working together in the fields, they entirely revolutionised the growing of wheat in India, among many other things. They improved both the strains and the yield. Later they were to spend half the year in Baluchistan, observing the local landworkers and learning from them, studying drainage and the aeration of soils, assisting the development of a fruit-growing industry.

Mr Howlett was on sick leave in Britain at this time. It is clear from all their joint publications and pronouncements that he and Harold too worked very comfortably together. They were probably also great friends, as the following anecdote suggests.

> At Pusa the snakes would climb up to the top of the door and drop on you if you were unlucky. I don't recall my father ever having an adventure of this sort but I feel he must have done. He had incredible powers of concentration, especially when he was talking. He was once walking with Howlett in a ruined brick tank and went over to look at something, disturbing a cobra's nest. Howlett saw this but Father didn't. But Howlett pulled him out.

One of Harold's enquiries, made in the previous year in conjunction with the Imperial Agricultural Chemist, was to be of importance later. It was into the drying of wheat before storage. The Wheat Weevil thrives only in damp conditions and the problem was to discover at what point in the drying the conditions became intolerable to the weevil.

From Harold's Summary of the year 1909–10, we learn that the culture of silk continued at Pusa, though on a small scale. They were now principally occupied in observing the different species. The culture of lac also continued. They had been studying the White Ant, the Dusky Ground Beetle and the Deccan Grasshopper. They were experimenting with and testing insecticides made from local materials. A Bengali edition of *Indian Insect Pests* had appeared, edited by Mr C.C. Ghosh, and the issue of coloured pictures of insect pests had proved to be very popular. Work on the biting flies was held up, in the absence of the Second Imperial Entomologist.

The status of the Research Institute at this time may perhaps be gauged by the following correspondence.

In January, the Secretary of State for India wrote, to the Government of India:

> I desire to receive the views of your Excellency's Government as to the best mode of making provision for the appointment as circumstances may permit of natives of India to posts in the Indian Agricultural Service, which at present are held by experts appointed by the Secretary of State in Council in this country. None has so far been appointed. But requests are being received from qualified Indians who have studied in the United Kingdom.

Not until September did Government reply to London. It was

> premature at present to recruit Indians for higher posts in the Indian Agricultural Service, though this is the ultimate goal. Pusa has only been operating for two years, and it is too early to fix rates of pay for students who have trained there. Five hundred rupees a month has been found sufficient. It is too early to offer higher rates for posts for which no Indians are yet qualified, and still more inadvisable to declare that officers recruited in India should be eligible for the same rates as experts from the United Kingdom. It is too early to make changes.

Acknowledging the report from Pusa for the years 1907–9, Government noted, again in January, 'with satisfaction the valuable assistance rendered by Messrs. Butler and Lefroy to the Provincial Department of Agriculture, and the former for the success which has attended the campaign carried out by the Government of Madras at his advice against the dangerous palm disease in the Godavari Delta, and Lefroy deserves much credit for his important work, *Indian Insect Life*.' By now nineteen students had been admitted to the College and Government regarded its development as more important than research.

In March a request was received from the Salvation Army to extend the Tata Silk Farm in Bangalore. They needed money for student quarters and new buildings for the weavery and for breeding and reeling. It was still a small farm at this time, with only a few acres of mulberry bushes, and the manager was Japanese. They mentioned that they had been in touch with Harold at Pusa about the cultivation of the Eri silkworm for the future, but this was yet to be established. In this case, however, Government was unable to help. They had recently been spending public funds on the silk industry in Bengal, Eastern Bengal and Assam and could not extend this to Mysore, which in any case was a native state. The Salvation Army was later to develop this silk farm, presumably from its own resources and those of the Tata Steel Company, into a flourishing concern.

On the 17th of May, the Inspector General suggested to the Revenue Department, India, that Mr F.M. Howlett, then on sick leave in the United Kingdom, should represent India at the International Congress of Entomology in Brussels in August. The Imperial Entomologist was a Life Member of that Congress and, as Second Imperial Entomologist, Mr Howlett was eminently suitable to represent him. This suggestion was referred to London, but not until July.

On the 19th of May, the Inspector General took up the question of Harold's honorarium.

> ... *Indian Insect Life* was issued in September 1909. From the press cuttings it will be seen how this great work has been welcomed and approved both by Indians and readers in other countries. Its production was as much a necessity for the improvement of the scientific side of entomology in India as that of *Indian Insect Pests* was for its applied side ...
>
> The book has been selling well. About 350 have already been sold, but the sales have hardly begun in Europe, America and the Colonies.

The publishers state that orders are coming in steadily and at the present rate the edition cannot last long.

The present edition is of one thousand, produced at a cost of Rs. 12,360. The price in India was fixed at Rs. 20, at £1.10.0d elsewhere. Of this Rs. 15 were credited to the Government. It was also agreed that the publishers would supply the Government with 340 copies free and fifty to newspapers and periodicals free of charge or commission. Thus the Government has received the equivalent of Rs. 7,800 and on the remaining six hundred and ten copies will realise (at Rs. 15 each) Rs. 9,150, or a net Rs. 16,950 against an initial expenditure of Rs. 12,360. The profit on this edition alone is Rs. 4500 leaving aside the incalculable gain to Indian agriculture. Both books have entailed on Mr. Maxwell-Lefroy heavy work in their production. Both were written in what should have been his leisure hours. But Mr. Maxwell-Lefroy has no leisure hours. I doubt whether any man in the service of the Indian Government puts in more hours of real work daily. These two works are a great credit to the Department. In sanctioning the publication of *Indian Insect Life* the Government suggested an honorarium but preferred to fix the amount after the book was published. In fixing the amount of the honorarium the loss to Mr. Maxwell-Lefroy of copyright of the two books has to be taken into consideration. Also Mr. F.M. Howlett contributed about 150 pages of *Indian Insect Life*. Any honorarium should be shared: I suggest one fifth to Mr. Howlett. I beg to strongly recommend Rs. 1000 for *Indian Insect Pests* and Rs. 5000 for *Indian Insect Life*. Please obtain the sanction of His Majesty's Secretary of State for India … It will I hope be admitted that looking at the gain of Rs. 4500 and the copyrights of the two books the proposed honorarium is extremely moderate.

In October the Government agreed to an honorarium of 1,000 rupees for *Indian Insect Pests*, and in December Lord Crewe, then Secretary of State for India, agreed to 2,000 rupees for *Indian Insect Life*, with 500 for Mr Howlett.

Between the 4th and 6th of August, Mr Howlett did attend the *Premier Congrès Internationale d'Entomologie* in Brussels. Among its *Mémoires* can be found 'A Note on methods of preserving insects in tropical climates' by F.M. Howlett, and 'The Progress of Economic Entomology in India' by Harold Maxwell-Lefroy and F.M. Howlett.

This neatly sums up Harold's work in India so far, as he was the first person to put any accumulated knowledge into practice.

It starts by saying that 62 per cent of the population is engaged in agriculture of one kind or another, and that there are four kinds of cultivator – the smallholder, the tenant farmer, the large landowner and the European planter, the latter in negligible numbers. The resources in the village are extremely limited so that they are, for instance, even unable to supply soap for spraying.

> Indian prejudice and misunderstanding is a special factor to be reckoned with, and it can only be countered by proving the cash value of a crop that has been saved. The idea of looking at crops while they grow and checking for insect pests is totally foreign to Indian cultivators. The government exercise control by means of a revenue collector in every village – a system the British took over from the native rulers. The collector is responsible for the welfare of the village and he reports to the Department of Agriculture when a crop is attacked by pests. The Agricultural Department was founded to study and to improve methods of agriculture in India, to test new methods, introduce new crops, and to teach the best methods. Each province has several English officers: agricultural botanists, chemists and native staff. The entomological section directs and controls the work all over India, testing remedies, methods, studying life histories, and all scientific work. The Provincial Departments investigate outbreaks, advise and collect local information.

A number of their successes are mentioned, including the invention of the Bag Method, for use with Locusts and the Rice Grasshopper. A large cloth bag is attached to two horizontal poles, one at either side, and drawn through the crop. Two men go ahead to drive the insects towards the bag and two others, or possibly three, drag it forward.

The moths from the Hairy Caterpillar only emerge at the first rain to lay their eggs and they have been successfully collected using a light trap. The ravages of the Potato Moth have been much reduced by the dry storage method. For the first year, the Agriculture Department supervised and bore the cost of storing, but since then the villagers, particularly in the Central Provinces, had adopted the method.

Measures against the Cotton Bollworm have included the destruction of all plants still standing in January, in order to prevent hibernation as larva or pupa; the planting of *bhindi* (*Hibiscus esculentes*) as a trap crop, destroying it before the cotton flowers; re-establishing its parasite, which had disappeared, it was thought, as a result of the abnormally cold conditions. It was sent to the Punjab, for instance, in *bhindi* pods. The planting of *bhindi* was not generally successful, as it needed watering, but where it was grown it succeeded. In a single year, the Bollworm was reduced to its usual level by the use of some, or all, of these methods.

'India could produce large quantities of long-stapled cotton if the Boll Worm could be controlled. At present only short-stapled cotton is grown as it matures quickly, and offers little chance to the Boll Worm.'

For the Mango Mealy Bug, *Monophebus octocaudata*, an enemy of both the mango and the jackfruit,

> Two simple remedies have been worked out: banding the tree-trunks to prevent the bugs climbing down to lay their eggs and destroying the eggs themselves, which are laid in the debris at the foot of the tree.
>
> These are instances of the work being done in India now. Only a little can be achieved by publications; cultivators need to be shown the methods, to have pressure put on them, and frequently one has to do the work, either with them or for them.
>
> Insecticides are very little known or used in India. We introduced kerosene emulsion; at first we had it made in England, now it is made locally. We keep a sharp eye on useless insecticides which come to our notice, and also on sprayers.
>
> Fumigation is not practised in India, either for buildings or plants, but there is a limited use of carbon bisulphide for grain.
>
> A separate branch at Pusa is concerned with insects that affect the health of man and domestic animals, the insects sucking the blood and possibly transmitting disease. But little has been done so far, except to identify them.

In the last seven years changes have become evident: many have read something, many are interested. More people now know that a caterpillar becomes a moth, which lays eggs. But in a population of three hundred million the idea of taking an interest in nature is wholly foreign; only the government and our department take an interest. But once trained students emerge from Agricultural Colleges and become officials there will be progress.

In addition to *destructive* insects, we are working on *productive* insects. Sericulture (silk production) is a big industry, and there are possibilities with bee-keeping. We are concerned to introduce sericulture to new localities, and have a centre to teach those who would like to take it up. We advise on suitable localities, and we sell two machines, now patented, for cleaning Eri cocoons and spinning. With mulberry silk, we are still only experimenting.

Lac is produced in India to the value of 3 million pounds. At present it is mainly a forest product, not properly grown. We have shown that it can be produced more cheaply by proper cultivation on trees in pastures and waste lands.

Bee-keeping is mainly the concern of the Forestry Department, as it is probably best suited to the hill tracts of India.

Above all, we have to reply courteously to every enquiry, to miss no opportunity of showing the value of our work – from ants eating sugar to an outbreak of army worm over a hundred thousand acres. Our list shows 104 important pests, of which the life history is now known of 74. We have prepared coloured plates of 75, and 65 of these are available now. We have simple easy methods of destruction of 40 pests, and we are working on a further 21 in the field to find effective measures which can be adapted to different conditions.

We have large reference collections. We have had to publish *Indian Insect Life* to meet the needs of our students and fellow-workers in India. What the future will be it is impossible to say. The time is ripe to de-centralise, to develop in the provinces the work we have done at Pusa. But here we explain the past, and do not attempt to sketch future possibilities.

In September 1910 a *Bulletin* was issued, attempting to connect the insects known all over India by different vernacular names with existing scientific information and nomenclature, a formidable task. In his introduction, Harold asked for comments and corrections, and gave directions for sending specimens to Pusa.

There had been a correspondence earlier in the year, to the effect that it was difficult to keep staff at Pusa as there was no adequate schooling for their children. The nearest Middle English School was ten miles away, and the nearest English High School twelve, long distances when all transport was horse-drawn. Now, in November, Government agreed to provide a Middle English School at Pusa itself, catering for more than the twenty-six boys already there. English, Hindi and Bengali were to be taught.

But, on the 10th of November, Denis Charles, Harold and Kathleen's elder son, died. Cecil, the remaining child, was swept up into the mists of Darjeeling, to be cared for by the nuns of the Loreto Convent where, later, Mother Theresa of Calcutta was to pass her novitiate. His parents, numbed and overwhelmed, remained at Pusa, desolately wondering what they should do next.

There is a legend in the family that Denis died from a 'fly-borne disease', which might account for Harold's passionate hatred of the housefly. This suggests that it was typhoid. Two other possibilities are dysentery and diphtheria. The fact that Cecil was removed so instantly rather points to the latter, which is highly infectious; and we should not forget that a child of Mr S.C. Misra also died, presumably from a similar infectious disease. Whatever the cause, we shall never know it for certain. The death certificates of both Denis and Gladys Elizabeth, if they still exist at all, are in the hands of the Roman Catholic authorities in India.

In the event, Harold put in for home leave, his first since his arrival in India. This was granted and the family sailed for England very early in 1911.

They took a house at Strawberry Hill, on the Thames between Teddington and Twickenham.

We were living in a house at Strawberry Hill, somewhere on the Thames. And I remember there was a heavy fall of snow. Well, nobody I knew had ever seen snow before. So Father made a snowman. And what I particularly remember – this is really the first time he swam into focus you might say – he was smoking a pipe and he took this thing out of his mouth and shoved it into the snowman's. I thought this frightfully funny and said 'Goodness, it's Dad'. And that's really my first recollection of him.

It was at Strawberry Hill that I first experienced racism when some small boys collected as we were sitting on the Embankment and jeered at my Indian *ayah* Elizabeth. 'Ya blackie.' I prepared to give battle but Elizabeth dragged me away.

CHAPTER XI

Harold had been granted three months' privilege leave from the 31st of January 1911, followed by one year and six months furlough from the 1st of May. It was eleven full years since he had spent any time in England. His friend Dr David Sharp had retired to Brockenhurst, in the New Forest, but Dr Adam Sedgwick had recently (1909) moved from Cambridge to become Professor of Zoology at the newly formed Imperial College of Science and Technology in South Kensington.

It is reasonable to suppose that Harold had kept in touch with these two men during his years in the West Indies and in India, and it is certain that he wrote to Imperial College from Pusa, on the 7th of December 1910, accepting their proposal that he should give a course of lectures on Entomology to be completed by the 31st of August 1911, for £200.

Just before leaving Pusa, he drafted a note to the effect that entomological conditions in south India were so entirely different from those in the rest of that country that the existing knowledge of Indian insect pests hardly applied there. This was in reply to a request from the Government of Madras to the Government of India, for the appointment of a European entomologist. He also prepared a ten-page report on the subject and this was eventually forwarded to London, in the following March.

He must at this time have been considering the course his own life was to take. He had lost two children in India. He had completed in eight years what many entomologists at that time might have regarded as a life's work; that is to say, *Indian Insect Pests* and *Indian Insect Life*. He had written innumerable *Bulletins* and *Memoirs* apart from them. The Entomological Department at Pusa was flourishing; his first students were already leaving to work on their own account. He had demonstrated, at least to various authorities, that economic entomology was a vital and practical science, whose beneficial effects could be shown, and computed, in cold figures.

On the 2nd of March 1911, he delivered his Inaugural Lecture on Applied Entomology. He was described as a 'Special Lecturer on Entomology, Imperial College of Science and Technology, South Kensington, Imperial Entomologist for India (on leave)'.

> This lecture is the first of a series dealing with general entomology, with special reference to the application of the science to agriculture, commerce, medicine, and sanitation. There is at present no one general course of lectures or training in entomology as a special subject given in England, and it is fitting that such a course should be initiated at the Imperial College of Science and Technology, whose function is to provide the highest instruction in branches of science which have practical application.
>
> Entomology used to be concerned with the study of insects solely from the biological and systematic sides; that is, entomologists were more concerned with studying the habits of insects and with classifying them than they were with checking and controlling them or with exploiting them as part of the world's commerce.
>
> Even now the value of the economic entomologist and the part he plays in daily life is very little appreciated in this country; there is in England no Government Entomologist, no entomological experiment station, and no organisation which does for the country as a whole what economic entomologists do in India, in our Colonies, and in the United States.
>
> Applied entomology, which is a development of pure entomology, deals with insects which affect man; the greater number of insects affect man directly in no way at all; they have an indirect bearing on man, as they have

their part to play in the economy of the earth; they scavenge and cleanse the earth; they pollinate flowers and make possible the fruiting of many plants; they populate all parts of the earth's surface, except the sea, and in numbers of kinds, as in actual abundance, they exceed all other forms of animal life visible to the naked eye. In these respects they are of interest but not of direct importance, and while the study of insects is a fascinating branch of natural history, there would not be any necessity to have economic entomologists if they did no more.

It is only lately that the significance of the insect world has become apparent; and it is mainly owing to the immense importance of tropical entomology that the study of insects from the economic aspect has received its greatest impetus. The opening up to agriculture of new tropical countries, the increasing competition in the cultivation of tropical products, the discovery of the part played by insects in disseminating human disease, have brought entomology to the front, and have shown that, far from being a science concerned solely with the minute classification of interminable varieties and species, it is a science which has great significance for man, and one which requires to be developed in serious earnest if we are to be in a position to harvest our crops, to cope with disease, and to populate tropical areas successfully.

In closely cultivated countries with temperate climates, insects have not the significance that they have in newly-planted areas, and it is perhaps due to this that in the study of economic entomology England is somewhat behind America and some other nations.

A recent report puts the loss sustained in the United States from the pear thrips, a minor pest, at one million dollars annually, and in the United States, where the organisation of entomology renders figures available, the total loss from destructive insects is put at three hundred million dollars annually. In British India, the losses to the eight principal crops at a conservative figure amount to fifteen million pounds per annum, and to the country as a whole, in all crops, to well over double that amount. Were those losses unpreventable, these figures would be of no value, but very largely the losses are preventable, either by the individual action of farmers themselves or by collective action on the part of the people, aided by Government.

Year by year the successes of entomology grow greater; a notable case is the success of the collective action of the South African colonies against their locusts; the migratory locusts of North India and the Bombay locust are now fought successfully; the potato moth, which in India and Australia did so much damage, has been checked by simple means within the reach of the cultivator; the phylloxera of the vine and the woolly aphis of the apple have been met by the introduction of resistant stocks on which the pests will not live; and if there are many cases where remedies or preventives are as yet beyond the reach of the farmer or where no profitable remedy has been discovered, there are far more cases where remedies or preventives are applied with profit and success.

Flour, meat, dried fish, dried fruits, almost every form of food must be preserved very carefully if insects are not to infest it. We have had to deal with flour moth in flour mills, with beetles in brush factories, woollen clothing stores, and leather factories, with beetle in tobacco factories, and with boring beetles attacking bamboos, wood, and the like. In the tropics the white ant is a very destructive agent; a commission is working now on the railway sleepers problem in India, the white ants finding railway sleepers excellent food in some parts of the country, and this problem involves a very large amount of money.

We can do nothing until we know our insects, know how they live, where they lay their eggs, how long the eggs take to hatch, where the grub lives, how it feeds, how long it lives, and every detail of its life from start to finish... In India the cultivator will tell you that the caterpillar that bores in his canes comes from the well water he irrigates with; a little investigation shows that the caterpillar comes from eggs laid in clusters on the leaves of the cane, and that, with some borers at least, these eggs can be cheaply and simply removed.

There is no magic that we can use, no one perfect simple remedy that fits all cases, no universal insecticide; for each case careful study, then experiment in the field, and then, with the co-operation of the farmer, the testing and application of remedies on a large scale.

It is common knowledge now that malaria is communicated to man by the bite of one of several kinds of mosquitoes... Since this discovery was made, it has been found that other diseases are carried by mosquitoes and other biting insects; yellow fever is carried by a mosquito common in the tropics, so is filariasis by other common mosquitoes; the rat flea is the agent which spreads plague; the tiny midge of the genus *Phlebotomus* carries Pappatacci and similar fevers; the large flies of the genus *Glossina* carry sleeping sickness of man and similar trypanosome diseases of cattle, horses and dogs. The common bed-bug is suspected, but not definitely convicted, of carrying kala-azar and similar diseases.

The problem is, then, to a large extent, an entomological one, and so, in all insect-borne diseases, it is the insect we have to study and fight.

Let us see what occurs in plague. A plague rat, that is a rat infected with the plague germ, is, we will say, let loose in London or anywhere you please; its fleas suck its blood and draw in the plague germ; the rat gets worse and dies. As its body gets cold, the fleas leave it and seek another rat or some other warm animal on which they can live; they bite that animal and give it plague also, thereby infecting other fleas, which leave the rat when it dies. Now, were those fleas only to bite rats, the disease would stop there, but they do not. They bite man also, incidentally, and he gets plague, and probably dies of it. That is why in India, when rats begin to die, the people at once have to avoid being bitten by a flea from a dead plague rat, and if they are wise they leave their houses.

Instead of using disinfectant to kill the germ, which was supposed to live in the dirt of the house, we now use insecticides to kill the fleas and prevent them breeding.

Are we going to get more and more diseases communicated by insects, now confined to tropical jungles, but brought within our range by increasing means of communication? Is the yellow fever going to reach Indo-China and India, for instance, by means of infected mosquitoes carried by ships from the Panama Canal when that is opened? The yellow fever mosquito is already in India, but not the germ, and while a yellow fever patient cannot carry it a mosquito might.

If we are ever to colonise the tropics, if we are to people them with healthy races, to develop them agriculturally, and to render available the immense amount of raw material they are capable of producing for England's manufactures and trade, it will only be when we have organised the entomology and successfully tackled the insect transmitters of disease.

In England, if mosquitoes and sandflies do not bite, there are dangers of an equally serious nature from the house flies and flesh flies, which carry the typhoid germ. Flies which settle on food may carry and do carry germs on their feet and on their proboscis; the common fly should be vigorously exterminated and kept down, and in this respect there is very much to be done in this country.

Our Colonies recruit their entomologists from America or take untrained men who get their training from experience, which is an expensive way. We should be able to recruit our men from England, as we do with all other branches of science, and it should be here in England that the training in entomology which must be acquired before any practical work is possible should be available.

…we want to differentiate research from executive work, and not expect the same man to do research, teaching, executive work, and the administration of the pest Acts; we want to develop a class of what we may call executive entomologists for organising and carrying on campaigns; we want co-operation between different parts of the Empire, between England and the Colonies; but our greatest need at present is a training institution, a source of supply of young men properly trained in entomology and specially selected for the peculiar qualifications required in an economic entomologist.

It was a lecture, from which perhaps a quarter has been selected, that was listened to with great attention, in particular by Lord Cromer, who was in the chair. As Major Evelyn Baring, he had spent four years in India as private secretary to his cousin the Viceroy, Lord Northbrook; and he was later invited by another Viceroy, Lord Ripon, to be Financial Member of the Viceroy's Council. In this position he proved to be both wise and practical, but it is his role in Egypt and the Sudan, as Sir Evelyn Baring, that history principally remembers. As Earl of Cromer he retired from public service in 1907 and accepted, among other honorary posts, the chair of the Entomology Research Committee, in which capacity he attended Harold's lecture.

From the *Westminster Gazette* of the 8th of March 1911:

Lord Cromer, presiding the other day at a lecture – the first of a series that promises to be of great value – by Mr. H. Maxwell Lefroy, Imperial Entomologist to the Government of India, spoke of 'our deficiency in practical field-training in the methods of combating insect pests of all kinds,' of the lack of 'adequate facilities of study for the men who would desire to obtain a sound general training in entomology as a whole,' of the need of 'a more business-like appreciation of the value of economic entomology in this country,' and of the absence of 'experimental stations where the value of such work could be practically demonstrated.'

These references in themselves constituted a sufficiently formidable indictment; but they only touched upon the fringe of a very large and very important subject. Mr. Maxwell Lefroy himself, however, has much more to say on the matter. He is a slight, clean-shaven man of middle-age, full of enthusiasm for his subject, and earnestly voluble in discussing it. He is tanned by a dozen years of exposure to Indian and West Indian suns; and if a holiday has brought him from India that holiday is being spent in a small laboratory at the Royal College of Science, high above the roofs of South Kensington. It was here that he gave his views upon the matter to a representative of the *Westminster Gazette*.

'Lord Crewe, when he was Secretary of State for the Colonies,' Mr. Lefroy said, 'organised a Committee of Entomological Research for the Department. It is in connexion with that committee that Mr. Carnegie has offered to defray the expense of sending three or four young men to the United States for three years, that they may be thoroughly trained in practical methods of dealing with noxious insects. If we devoted more attention to the subject over here we might be able to train our own men, and to put their training to good use when they have acquired it. That is the object with which my course of lectures has been inaugurated by the Imperial College of Science and Technology – the first course of the kind to be given in England.'

The Mr Carnegie mentioned here was Mr Andrew Carnegie, an American multi-millionaire of Scottish origin, who had made his money in iron and steel, railroads and shipping. He considered that the duty of a man of wealth was 'to set an example of modest, unostentatious living, shunning display or extravagance; to provide moderately for the wants of those dependent upon him; and, after doing so, to consider all surplus revenues which come to him simply as trust funds, which he is called upon to administer...'; and in this spirit he endowed libraries all over the English-speaking world and set up innumerable trust funds, principally in the

United States, most of them with an educational purpose. His intervention in this case must be regarded as symptomatic of his excellent intentions.

Harold continued to lecture throughout 1911, in places such as Birmingham and Cambridge as well as in London. In one of them, also reported by the *Westminster Gazette* on the 11th of March, he mentioned that seven million pounds worth of damage had been done to cattle in the previous year by the Ox Warble Fly; and that the Diamond Back Moth had caused a loss of £90,000 to various crops in Aberdeenshire alone.

His activities were reported in India, in, for instance, *The Pioneer* of Allahabad. In addition to the subjects covered in his inaugural lecture, he returned to the subject of standardised nomenclature, first touched on by him in the *Journal of Economic Biology* in 1908: 'As the International Congress meets in Oxford in 1912 let us make a start. So many changes are taking place as new work is done, and since not everyone calls an insect by the same name there is confusion...'

On the 14th of June, just over a week before the Coronation of King George V, a Conference was held at the Colonial Office. Its members were many of the very distinguished men who had arrived to attend that Coronation. Its subject was to discuss how to improve co-ordination between the various countries of the British Empire in preventing the spread of all injurious insects, whether to agriculture or horticulture. The Chairman was once again Lord Cromer, who proposed that a central organisation should be established in London to collect and disseminate all relevant information. He gave the probable cost of such an organisation as £500 a year. He then invited the Imperial Entomologist to address them on the subject.

> Some time ago I had to prepare a scheme for India; and in preparing this scheme our greatest difficulty lay in knowing what plant imports to keep out of the country which might bring in disease...

The general principle which is adopted is, I think, to keep out everything that may in any way bring in any form of insect pest. My proposal is to substitute for that the transmission of accurate information regarding the actual pests occurring in all these countries, so that instead of blindly legislating against everything, it would be possible to discriminate between the imports which are safe and those imports which are definitely known to be capable of bringing in insect pests. The foundation of that scheme is, of course, accurate knowledge of the insect pests of each country...

It might appear that when we have got all this information the work would cease, but I think that it would lead inevitably to a further very important development and that is the exchange of information dealing with beneficial parasitic insects. We have in India a caterpillar which does us a great deal of harm, but we know it is checked by a parasite. That parasite we know does not occur in Egypt. If Egypt had that information it might import that parasite and so do the country a very great service. That sort of thing can be indefinitely multiplied, because for every one of those pests there are parasites; and I look forward to the future of this scheme as being eventually an exchange of parasites and things of that sort.

His speech was enthusiastically received by, among others, the Prime Ministers of New South Wales and Tasmania, the High Commissioner for New Zealand, the Minister for Education in South Africa, the Minister of Agriculture from Newfoundland, the Agents General for West and South Australia, the Minister of Agriculture from Ontario and the Under-Secretary for Finance and Trade in New South Wales.

As a result of this inaugural meeting, the Imperial Bureau of Entomology was set up in London in the following year, with its headquarters at the Museum of Natural History. It was to be of enormous value to economic entomologists the world over. Insects could be sent to it for examination and identification; and it published the *Review of Applied Entomology* monthly, in two parts, Agricultural and Medical & Veterinary. The actual details, in the first instance, were worked out by Harold himself, with a Dr Guy Marshall and a Sir H.J. Reid from the Colonial Office.

That his activities as a lecturer were reported back to Pusa is fairly certain. On the 15th of June, Mr Bernard Coventry, as Officiating Inspector General, wrote, to the Government of India:

> Mr. Maxwell-Lefroy has been eight years in the Department and has reached the pay ceiling. His pay is not adequate for an officer of his ability and experience and he has now reached a stage in his service at which the question of additional remuneration should be settled on so that he may be induced to stay in it...
>
> His enthusiasm in his branch of work has made itself felt everywhere. Besides having organised and established the section on Entomology at Pusa the Imperial Entomologist has had to scrutinise and criticise programmes of the work of entomological assistants throughout India, and this work is carried out in accordance with suggestions made by him from time to time and in close touch with that at Pusa. He has shown remarkable ability in organising campaigns against insect pests and in devising remedies within the reach of the Indian cultivators. The present position of Eri silk culture is mostly due to this officer...
>
> I feel no hesitation in saying that the loss to the Department would be irreparable if Mr. Maxwell-Lefroy were to leave it, which contingency is, I am afraid, not improbable if additional remuneration in recognition of his good service is not sanctioned.

Mr Coventry attached the formidable list of Harold's publications, his books, *Memoirs, Bulletins* and *Journal* articles. In October Lord Crewe sanctioned an extra allowance of 100 rupees a month, rising monthly by 20 rupees to 200 a month.

By the end of July, Harold was able to report very regular attendances at his classes at Imperial College. There were almost no absences and all the excursions for collecting purposes were fully subscribed. Practical work in the field aroused particular interest among the students, as did his lectures on injurious insects. He had by now completed his course of thirteen lectures. He had given two practical demonstrations in the Chelsea Physic Garden and had undertaken five and a half days of fieldwork.

On the 1st of September 1911, he was re-appointed lecturer for a further year by Imperial College, at an annual salary of £300.

At the beginning of the next year, he delivered a lecture to the West India Committee, in Seething Lane, EC, on the possibility of adding silk to the industries of the West Indies. The lecture was reported in *The Times*, the *Daily Telegraph* and, in particular, the *Financial Times*:

> Sir Frederic Hodgson, late Governor of British Guiana, presided, and said Mr. Lefroy was one of a batch of very able men who went out to work in the West Indies for the Imperial Department of Agriculture. Mr. Lefroy had served under Sir Daniel Morris, who had done so much to assist in the work of extricating the West Indian colonies from too much dependence on one industry. Mr. Lefroy's work in the West Indies was very soon recognised, and in a short time he was taken away by the Government of India.
>
> 'I would not discuss the subject at all,' [The lecturer said] 'unless I felt convinced that there were possibilities that merit serious attention; we do very little to stimulate the production of silk in the Empire; France does a great deal to foster it in her colonial possessions, and in Japan an immense industry has grown up. We have tried the same in India, but only on a small scale and without much in the way of expert assistance...
>
> I would suggest a trial which any West Indian planter could make, first, of simply rearing the best variety of silkworm on a small scale, say, with one ounce of seed. Rearing is not difficult, and could be looked after by any intelligent person who took the trouble to follow directions. If the worms did well and the cocoons were large, they should be sent for report to France...
>
> The West Indies have, above all, an enormous advantage in their splendid climate, and such an experiment, carefully carried out, would not involve an excessive expenditure.'

Harold is described at this time as being 'an energetic, insistent and forceful man, with strong individualistic ideas. He was fond of lecturing on the subject "The Training of an Economic Entomologist", and in those talks he told some very pertinent truths about the difficulties of an entomologist's tasks.'

Meanwhile, he engaged in battle with the authorities at Imperial College to separate the course in Entomology from the course in

Zoology. On the 12th of May 1912, he wrote to the Rector, Sir Alfred Keogh:

> I hope my point will not be lost sight of, that entomology should be a section, distinct from zoology, under the direction of the Professor in charge of Biology. I want to be as closely in touch with all branches of botany as possible. I want more help from them than from zoology, and I am not at all keen on being put in with zoology.

Harold had already asked for a further ten months' extension of his leave from Pusa. The Inspector General, whose post was about to be abolished, made no objection but, on the 29th of June, the Secretary of State in London telegraphed to the Viceroy, in Simla: 'Lefroy has applied to resign after six months with effect from the 15th of June. Asks permission to return to duty at once.'

On the 2nd of July the Agricultural Advisor replied to the Viceroy: 'Have no objection to urge. Have been informed Lefroy has accepted remunerative employment at home.'

On the 3rd of July the Viceroy suggested that Lefroy should resign from the end of his furlough, without returning to India.

On the 9th of July the Secretary of State telegraphed the Viceroy: 'Lefroy sailed P&O 5 July in anticipation of cancellation of leave. He did not report departure which I only learnt on endeavouring to communicate your wishes to him.'

On the 20th of July Mr Bernard Coventry, now Agricultural Advisor to the Government of India, proposed the appointment of Mr T. Bainbrigge Fletcher, Entomologist to the Government of Madras, as successor to Harold Maxwell-Lefroy.

On the 29th of July Harold arrived back, alone, in Pusa, three months and five days before the end of his leave. On the 15th of August he wrote from there to Imperial College, accepting his appointment as Professor of Entomology, a chair that had been created specifically for him. On the 30th of September, the Agricultural Adviser telegraphed to the Revenue Secretary: 'Lefroy must settle this week whether to accept the offer at home. Can you make him definite offer now?'

The offer was made, very promptly on the 2nd of October. Twelve hundred rupees a month from April 1912 was proposed, rising to 1,250 from April 1913 and to 1,500 in April 1918.

Harold requested two days to consider these terms but declined them, five days later. He asked for permission to leave the service on the 15th of December.

On the 10th of October Mr Bernard Coventry informed the Government of India: 'Lefroy not willing. Accept resignation and permit him to leave the Department 15 December 1912.'

At the end of October, Harold asked if he might leave on the 1st, rather than the 15th, of December. On the 6th of November this was agreed by Government.

He resigned as Imperial Entomologist on the 1st of December and it was therefore as Professor of Entomology at Imperial College that he landed in England later that month.

One would like to think that he was home in time for Christmas.

CHAPTER XII

Where did we go after Strawberry Hill? We moved to a house called Acton Lodge in Isleworth. That was a very big house with a large garden. That would be between 1912 and 1915. They had created this job for Father, you see, when he threw up his job in India. Two children had died. He decided, well, that if he stayed I would be the next one to go. So they created this job for him. So he had to be somewhere near South Kensington. He used to go by train but later on he lost no time in first of all acquiring motor bikes and then he went on to cars. He was mad keen and didn't need to bother with the public transport. As soon as he could get rid of it he did. It was open country with big fields between us and then a road called Syon Lane. There was a railway bridge on one side. I used to be taken for regular walks up Syon Lane by Elizabeth, my *ayah*. Until she could no longer stand the climate and returned, tearfully, to India. But the motor bikes. Poor Mother used to have to squeeze into the sidecar. With no protection against the wind she used to have to wear a hat with huge goggles and a veil and sometimes I squeezed in beside her. Our sidecar was very modern. You could fold the whole thing over – you really felt as if you were in a coffin. Only your head was sticking out. It upset Mother's complexion – she had to go and see a specialist. So she was very relieved when he moved on to cars. Slightly less dangerous.

It is not clear where the Professor's mother was living at this time. Wherever it was, she was alone. Her daughter had married and Patrick, her youngest son – described as 'lively, attractive and the greatest fun' – was at sea, a Lieutenant in the Royal Navy. Three of her sons were distantly abroad, in Tasmania, Canada and India; the fourth was also a serving officer in the Navy, having recently attained the rank of Captain.

While the Professor certainly took his family to see her, she had apparently no accommodation to offer. They were to live always in furnished houses, larger or smaller as prosperity dictated.

Now he concentrated on establishing his department at Imperial College and on the problem of finding suitable students.

On the 8th of February 1913, *The Spectator* published a letter from him:

> We receive many enquiries from parents about the prospects of a career in economic entomology, and I trust you will be able to give publicity to this subject.
>
> There are prospects for a limited number of young men to secure appointments as economic entomologists under the Colonial and Indian Governments, on pay usually from £300 upwards. Those are Civil Service appointments, mostly in the Agricultural Department. The essential qualifications are:
>
> 1. A degree in science (including zoology and botany) or its equivalent.
> 2. A post-graduate training in entomology, such as is given at this College.
> 3. A genuine keenness for the subject.
>
> This last is the most important, and it is on that account I desire to draw attention to this subject. There is a very small number of boys to whom insects are of fascinating interest – so fascinating that they really care for little else; these are the boys we want and it is this career which opens a prospect of utilizing a boy's bent to the best advantage. It is necessary to guard against magnifying the natural interest of nearly all boys in silkworms, etc., into this larger interest, and assuming that one's boy is an embryo entomologist.
>
> We want a dozen or so a year, and we want the 'freak' boy really; there are such boys, a very, very few, and it is to draw the attention of their parents that I write now. In addition, it is essential that the boy should be a gentleman and able to ride. It is clear that the British parent has not

realised that an opening exists or its limitations; at present it is difficult to get the right men for the post. We want to secure a supply of the right men for posts hereafter, and my appeal is to the parents of the right boy, aged now between 12 and 18.

By the end of October, the Professor had answered seventy-one replies to this letter.

The requirement that 'the boy should be a gentleman and able to ride' was not a simple, snobbish demand. Anyone then arriving in India, or in any of the overseas Colonies, particularly those in Africa, and unable to ride a horse would have been at the most tremendous disadvantage. It remained almost the sole source of transport. Entomologists, in particular, would have been required to visit localities inaccessible even by bicycle. The term 'gentleman' here must mean 'one who has attended a Public School' as this peculiarly rigorous form of education was an essential introduction to life in the Empire. It also produced a type of man able to give instructions and to see that they were carried out, an indispensable quality at that time.

The £300 mentioned in the letter was by no means an ungenerous starting salary. The Professor himself, we learn from Imperial College files, was being paid £600, Professor Sedgwick £800 and the lecturers £300.

Entomology, in spite of the letter written to the Rector a year previously, was still 'put in with zoology'. The course proposed for an ARCS (Associate of the Royal College of Science) in Entomology was for four years, in which entomology was studied only in the fourth. The first year included Chemistry, Mechanics or Mathematics, Physics and Organic Chemistry. The second year consisted of Botany, Zoology, Geology and Embryology. The third year was devoted to Zoology, the study of the entire animal kingdom.

In the fourth year, between October and December, Helminthology (the study of worms) occupied two mornings a week, Arachnids (spiders) one morning and General Entomology two mornings or afternoons. Between January and March, Cytology (the study of cells) and Histology (of organic tissues) occupied two mornings, Plant Pathology (diseases of) two mornings or afternoons, Systematic Entomology two afternoons and the study of *Diptera*, the Blood-Suckers, two afternoons. Between April and June, Protistology, the study of the Protozoa and the Protophyta, took up two mornings, Plant Physiology two mornings and the Economic Entomology Course two afternoons, in the week.

Five distinct courses in Entomology were on offer.

The General Course consisted of twenty lectures with practical work, on Tuesday and Thursday afternoons, between 2 and 5 p.m. The course ended on the 20th of March.

The Systematic Course contained twenty lectures, also with practical work. It reviewed the groups of insects, their diagnosis, colour and appearance, internal and external structures, sex distinction, life history, food habits, their natural enemies and other methods of control, appropriate literature and their economic importance.

The Economic Course also consisted of twenty lectures with practical work, partly in the field. The lectures covered the economic importance of insects and the principal groups concerned; pests of the world's crops, of man himself and of domestic animals; insects which transmit disease; insecticides, fumigants and existing legislation; the work of a Government Entomologist; and office methods, the preparation of illustrations and the literature of Entomology.

There were eighteen lectures in the Short Course in Entomology, also with practical work – nine days in the field in three, or three and a half, consecutive weeks, including Saturdays, 10 to 1 p.m. and 2 to 5, in July, August and September. A specific course on the cockroach was offered again, having been given in 1911, but only if required.

The Short Course in General Entomology had eighteen lectures with practical work, nine days in the field in three, or three and a half, consecutive weeks, also in July, August or September,

The last two courses were only to be arranged if enough students enrolled to make them self-supporting. The fees were between

£2.10s.0d and £3 a month, and it was hoped to attract officers from the Colonies and Indian services who were home on leave and wished to qualify in Tropical Entomology.

It is not clear how many, if any, assistants the Professor had in carrying out this programme. It is certain that all the lectures were delivered by him, and that he supervised all the fieldwork. It is a formidable timetable for one man, or even for two; but we must suppose that his immense enthusiasm carried him through.

This was to be the basis of his life for the future. Unless specifically granted leave of absence by Imperial College, he fulfilled his teaching commitments punctiliously; his first responsibility was to his students. All the other posts, or positions, which he took on, honorary or otherwise, were in addition to, were over and above, his situation as an active, teaching professor.

He received a blow, however, at the end of February. Adam Sedgwick, his friend and mentor since Cambridge days, died abroad. He had completely re-organised the Department of Zoology at Imperial College since his arrival there as Professor in 1909, and it is probable that Harold did not object too much to being 'put in with zoology' so long as the Professor was Adam Sedgwick. He had gone abroad at the end of the previous year, in an attempt to recover his health. He had not succeeded.

Twenty-two years older than Harold, *The Times* referred to him as 'more of a pioneer and prophet. He had to a high degree the gift of inspiring affection, and his very eccentricities seemed only to endear him the more to his attached pupils and friends.' He was to be very much missed.

In March, the Indian Department of Agriculture published one of Harold's last *Journals* as Imperial Entomologist. It was written with his brother-in-law, R.S. Finlow, described as the Fibre Expert to the Government of Bengal. It was an *Inquiry into the insecticidal action of some mineral and other compounds on caterpillars* and was an account of experiments made to determine how far other substances than arsenic were poisonous to plant-feeding insects. It is pleasant to know that the two men were on sufficiently good terms to be able to collaborate on such a project.

By May of that year, the fieldwork was well advanced. On the 13th *The Star* reported:

> The Ham Cross Oak Plantation in Richmond Park was yesterday the scene of an extremely interesting experiment. Last year the plantation was defoliated by swarms of caterpillars, so H.M. Office of Works sought the aid of Professor Maxwell Lefroy, of the Imperial College of Science at South Kensington. The trees have been under observation for some time, and a number of different specimens have been hatched out by the students at the college under the Professor, with the result that many different kinds of caterpillars and insects have been 'placed'. Yesterday, armed with a spray pump and miles of hose, the students under the direction of the Professor, delivered lead chromate in solution from six different hose branches, each branch spraying one gallon a minute on the affected trees.
>
> The operations were watched by representatives of the Office of Works, the park keeper, and other gentlemen interested in park lands, and the system will probably be extensively used in the future. The chemical does the trees no harm, but insects feeding on the poisoned leaves are killed. Branches from the trees will be taken to the Imperial College of Science after having been poisoned, and extensive experiments will be carried on by the students under Professor Lefroy by feeding different insects on the leaves and noting the effects. The operations are especially interesting, as the system of spraying with suitably selected chemicals is of course of vast importance to growers of commercial trees, such as fruit and rubber trees.

A photograph accompanied this report, of the Merryweather Petrol Spray Pump, about the size of a small tractor with iron wheels, two much larger than the other two. Another report, sadly incomplete, and under the heading 'A "Murderer" of Millions' mentions that:

> Saunterers in the neighbourhood of the oak wood at Ham Cross, Richmond Park, yesterday, astonished by the sight of a fire brigade ladder among the trees and a party of men who seemed to be busily

dousing the new green foliage, went out of their way to see what it was all about. What they found was Professor Lefroy, of the Imperial College of Science, directing a number of entomological students in the art of putting out the light of a great plague of caterpillars with a petrol-driven pump.

Cecil recollects:

> That was when Father started to make his name and I remember we had visitors who came down quite a lot. I was quite small, of course, and didn't really take any part. He used to get his students down. He did a lot of lecturing and his students were popping in the whole time. He went to Germany. I think he'd been at school there. What he went for of course I don't know. All I remember was he brought back this super electric train and he rigged it up in an attic and used to spend an awful lot of time playing with it. He'd rigged it up and everything. It was a marvellous train. We had a short circuit once and there was fire and smoke and I ran out of the room. Usually I just sat there watching while he played with it. It had an accumulator, a proper acid thing. I'd never seen one of these before. Must have been the latest technology. Then something went *pouff* and I thought, well – I don't want any more technology.

In January of that year, a certain Sir James Caird, first and only baronet of Roseangle, Dundee, who had made a fortune in the jute trade in India, gave £1,000 to the Zoological Society with which to build an additional Insect House at the London Zoo.

The existing building was described as 'a green-house heated to suffocation in order that tropical cocoons may hatch.' There were no satisfactory models. In general insect houses were simply heated apartments with museum showcases round the walls. By July, however, it was decided that the building should be L-shaped and next to the Small Mammals House, so that the heating could be shared; and the Professor agreed to act as Honorary Curator.

The building was completed in October. The shaded passage-ways for the visitors had, down both sides, a series of compartments, each with its own temperature and humidity.

On the 6th of October, *The Times* reported:

One of very few images that exist of Harold Maxwell-Lefroy, who hated the camera. This poor reproduction is from a textbook on Agricultural Entomology by Hem Singh Pruthi.

Harold's mother, Elizabeth Catherine Maxwell-Lefroy, in 1903.

Family collection

Helen Ormerod, respected entomologist whose studies, begun as an amateur, were widely influential in the study of insects at the time when Harold was first developing his interest.

Royal Entomological Society

Claude Grahame-White, pioneer aviator and schoolfriend of Harold's.

Collection of Dave Lam

Vauxhall Bridge, opened in 1816 and known originally as Regent Bridge, was designed by Harold's paternal great-grandfather, James Walker, a renowned civil engineer.

Engraving by James B. Allen from a painting by Thomas Hosner Shepherd

George Nathaniel, Lord Curzon, *left*, Viceroy of India at the time of Harold's arrival.

Sir Daniel Morris, *right*, Agricultural Adviser to the Colonial Office.

© National Portrait Gallery, London

Albert Howard, Biological Botanist at the Agricultural Research Institute, Pusa.

The Great Granary at Bankipore, built by John Garstin of the Bengal Engineers in 1786.

British Library

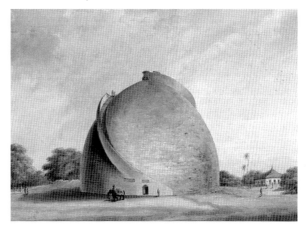

Andrew Carnegie, *left*, wealthy American industrialist who funded the training of British entomologists in the United States.

Library of Congress

Evelyn Baring, Lord Cromer, *right*, chair of the Entomology Research Committee and a supporter of Harold's work.

The Pusa Institute, c.1927.

Sir Peter Chalmers Mitchell, *left*, Secretary of the Zoological Society and founder of Whipsnade Zoo.

Herbert Samuel (later Sir, then Viscount), *right*, President of the Local Government Board during Harold's First World War fly-reduction campaign.

George Grantham Bain Collection

clockwise from above

SS *Salsette*, the P&O liner on which Harold and Kathleen sailed to India in November 1915 to take up the post of Imperial Silk Specialist.
Collection of Carolla Ingall

W.W. Froggatt, Government Entomologist for New South Wales, with whom Harold endured a strained relationship during his time in Australia.
Sydney Morning Herald

Evelyn Cheesman, head of the Insect House at London Zoo, who began her work there under Harold's direction.

Queen Mary recycles her feathers, at the investiture of the Prince of Wales and the Delhi Durbar, both in 1911 – or was it the same hat? The use of feathers was a controversial millinery practice on which Harold expressed himself.

Mary Field, *below*, naturalist filmmaker with whom Harold collaborated on *Secrets of Nature*, a series of short films.

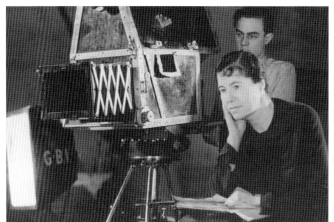

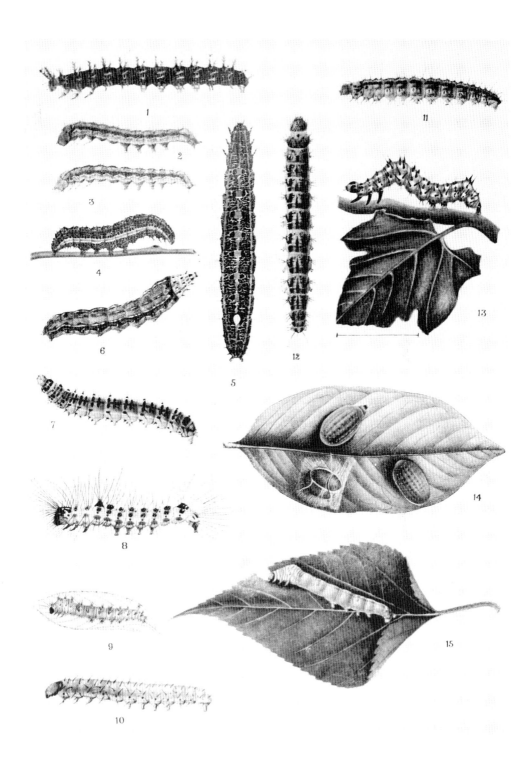

Indian Insect Life, plate, 'Caterpillars'.

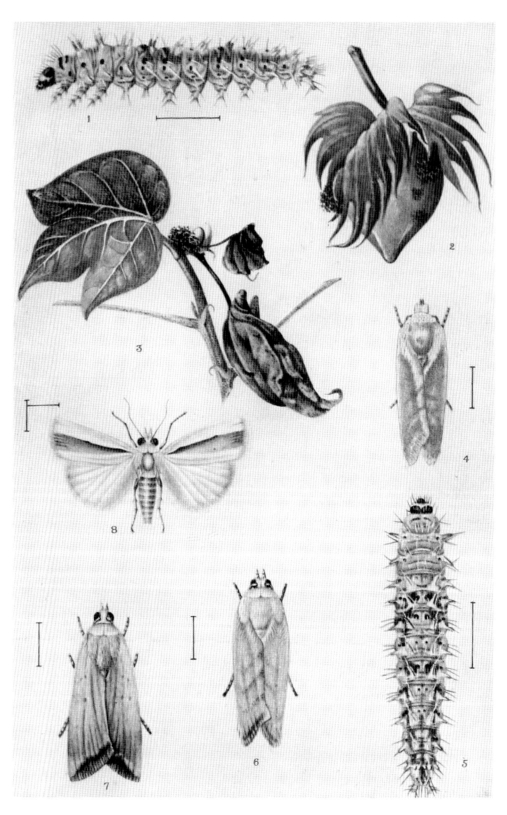

Indian Insect Life, plate, 'Cotton Boll Worm'.

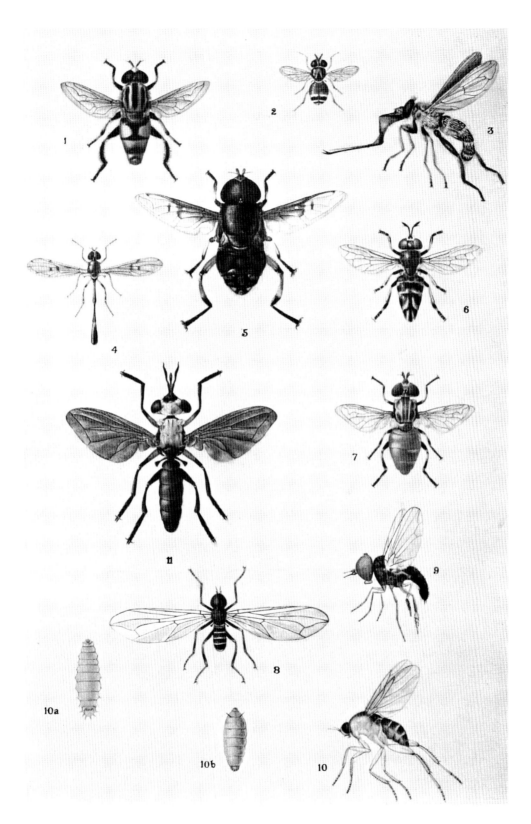

Indian Insect Life, plate, 'Syrphidae etc.'.

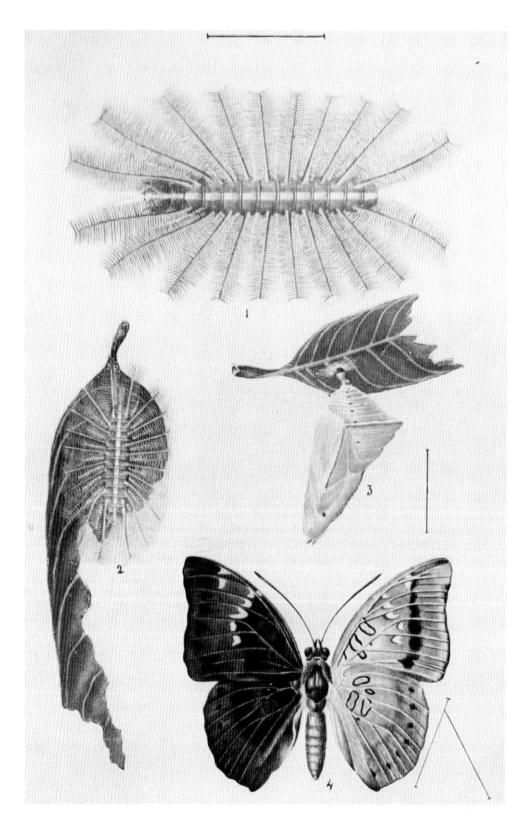

Indian Insect Life, plate, 'Euthalia-garuda'.

Professor Lefroy and his assistants are at work arranging the first set of exhibits. Arrangements have been made for entomologists from all over the world to send tropical insects in their resting stage. One of the largest compartments – for the peacock butterfly – is already occupied. There is turf on the floor and flowers in pots are sprayed every day with syrup.

There were explanatory diagrams, one of which stated simply that an insect was a small invertebrate animal with a head, a thorax and an abdomen, with six legs on the thorax and either two or four wings. The compartments for stick insects, scorpions, spiders and certain caterpillars were completed before the public were admitted on the 9th of October. The grounds round the Insect House were still being laid out but Sir James Caird, presumably delighted with the way his money had been spent, donated a further £500 and was made an Honorary Fellow of the Society. The Insect House quickly became one of the most popular features at the Zoo.

The Imperial Bureau of Entomology continued to make progress, with Dr Guy Marshall as Director. Its Report for 1913 states that the Management Committee represents the self-governing dominions and India, and that Professor Maxwell-Lefroy represents India.

The regulations and laws against injurious insects were still under very serious discussion and the Bureau had extended its activities, to the point where a Major S.P. James, of the Indian Medical Service, had been sent by the Indian Government to Central and South America to report on the possibility of yellow fever being introduced to India on the opening of the Panama Canal.

Mr F.W. Fiske, an entomologist from the United States, was in Nyasaland investigating the tse-tse fly, its effects on human beings and on cattle. It was hoped that this would be the beginning of a well-organised campaign against the tse-tse fly, whose existence prevented the opening up to agriculture of large areas of East Africa.

Eighty thousand specimens had been sent to the Bureau for identification. Mr Andrew Carnegie had renewed, for a further three years, his offer to send young British entomologists to be trained in

America. Dr Guy Marshall had visited the West Indies and, as a result of his visit, had been able to show 'that the beetle, *Phytalus*, which was devastating the sugar-cane in Mauritius, was indigenous in Barbados, and in a larva he brought home a parasite was found … Consignments of the parasite have now been sent to Mauritius and there is every hope that the species may be successfully established in that island.'

At about this time a Plumage Bill was introduced to the House of Commons. A previous one, introduced to the Lords in 1907, had failed to reach the Commons.

Feathers had recently been an important adjunct to high fashion. A long-handled fan of the 1880s, for instance, was made from the feathers of the scarlet ibis, trimmed with swansdown and with a stuffed hummingbird mounted in the middle. A muff of the 1890s was made from sealskin trimmed with grebe feathers, and the Edwardian lady's hat had expanded, between 1900 and 1910, to proportions unknown since the 1780s, or at least since the 1830s.

It was possibly at its maximum extension, sideways, at the Black Ascot of 1910, when Society went into mourning for King Edward VII. Hats were trimmed with artificial flowers, ribbon, tulle, artificial fruit and enormous *cloisonné* insect brooches, secured with vast jewelled hat pins, real and otherwise; but, above all, they were trimmed with feathers, many of them from wild birds, lyre-birds, birds of paradise, kingfishers, sooty terns, humming-birds, egrets and herons, some species of which were by now in danger of extinction.

The Society for the Protection of Birds, founded in 1889, received its Royal Charter in 1904. Two years later the Queen, Alexandra, undertook never to wear osprey feathers or indeed any feathers which involved the death of the bird. 'Osprey,' thundered a leading article in *The Times*, 'is the meaningless millinery term for the nuptial plumage of white egrets.'

Queen Mary, Queen Alexandra's successor, followed her example; and, while the hat she wore at the inauguration of her son as Prince of Wales in 1911 must have been one of the largest ever known in the history of millinery, it was decorated only with ostrich feathers. The feather boa, too, hallmark of high fashion for several years, was rarely made from anything other than ostrich feather tips. Ostrich feathers were acceptable: they were 'cut from the living animal and the stumps removed later'.

In a leading article on the 5th of December 1913, *The Times* strenuously supported the Plumage Bill.

> It aims at preventing the importation of feathers used in millinery which are obtained from wild birds, often in circumstances of great cruelty, but does not interfere with unobjectionable industries such as the trade in ostrich plumes…A law has been enacted in the United States prohibiting the import of plumage, while local legislation there for the protection of threatened species has been enforced more extensively and thoroughly… the traffic stands plainly revealed as one of the most wantonly cruel of modern days.

It concluded:

> All legitimate methods of breeding birds for their plumage can be safeguarded as definite exceptions under an Act prohibiting importation; and only the exclusion by law of all plumage not so specified can put this country abreast of the United States and of its own daughter Dominions in the supply of a barbarous industry.

Having once put the case against all importation of plants into India, on the ground that benevolent insects might be excluded, the Professor now put the case against the 'exclusion by law of all plumage' on the ground that something malevolent might be included.

The Times published his letter on the 8th of December.

> Surely it is possible to discriminate between those species of birds which are in danger of being exterminated or in the taking of whose plumage there is wanton cruelty, and those in which there is no such thing. Is it also reasonable to use as an argument in this case the cruel practice referred to as having occurred once in Karachi of sewing up birds' eyes? It would be equally reasonable to stop the consumption in India of all birds because cases are known of turkeys being killed for table by plucking out their tongues. Is it really reasonable to stop the whole importation

of plumage on cases such as this, and would it not be simpler to stop the cruelty itself? I have no direct knowledge of the wanton cruelty involved in the getting of special plumage, but I have a little experience of Indian birds. The most directly destructive bird in India is the rose-ringed parroquet, whose plumage used to be exported; there is no doubt that the extermination of 90% of this bird would be a great benefit to the Indian cultivator. Why, then, stop the export from India or the import to England of its plumage; why not discriminate reasonably? I believe no Bill would be opposed that was sane and reasonable, but it looks as if such a Bill were impossible.

This letter does not seem to have sparked off any further correspondence, although feelings on the subject were high and were to get higher. *The Times* leader was answered on the 9th of December, by a letter expressing 'the views of the trade'. 'Why should bird-farming be banned and fur-farming blessed? Fur-bearing animals must be killed; birds moult annually…The only bird where killing is associated with cruelty is egrets in Venezuela in the breeding season…We intend to fight to a finish. We will accept any sane regulations.'

The feather trade at that time was worth approximately £2,000,000 a year, and the dispute was to rumble on for many years to come.

Meanwhile, the hats of 1913 were smaller than those of 1912, though they supported some high feathers. Emphasis shifted from the brim to the crown, and simple elegance, rather than undisguised display, became the aim of high fashion. Feathers gradually fell out of favour.

CHAPTER XIII

By now the importance of entomology in colonial administration was fully understood, at least in Britain. An interesting statistic exists for West Africa, where the death-rate from insect-borne diseases was, in 1896, ninety per thousand. In 1904, it was twenty-eight per thousand but by 1911 was only fourteen per thousand. In India alone there were by now forty scientific posts, mycologists, entomologists, economic botanists, cotton specialists and agricultural chemists. In East Africa, however, where the Germans had also set up a colony, in Tanganyika, the great bar to development was the existence of the tse-tse fly. The control, or elimination, of this insect, which carried the disease known as 'sleeping sickness', became a matter of the first urgency.

Mr F.M. Howlett, who had written the section on the blood-sucking flies, the *Diptera*, in *Indian Insect Life* – although the genus *Glossina* did not occur in India – was still in India. The American entomologist, Mr F.W. Fiske, was in Nyasaland, studying the tse-tse fly at first hand, so it fell to the Professor, as one of the few people in Britain who knew anything about the subject at all, to answer questions from a Departmental Committee on Sleeping Sickness.

Several people gave evidence to this Committee, Dr Guy Marshall, Director of the Imperial Bureau of Entomology, game wardens, veterinary surgeons and medical people of various kinds. On the 12th of

December 1913, the Professor appeared before it, the Chairman being the Earl of Desart, last of a line of Irish Peers, then aged sixty-five.

Chairman: We are extremely obliged to you, Professor Lefroy, for coming to help us today. Among other problems which we have to deal with, and perhaps the most important of all, is the possibility of being able to eliminate or deal with the fly so as to render it non-effective. I understand that you have been good enough to write to the Secretary of State that you have not yourself personal experience of the tse-tse fly.

Professor: No, I have none.

Chairman: Your very large experience has been in dealing with insects in other parts of the world, but you have read, I presume, the literature.

Professor: Yes, I have read a good deal of the literature.

The interview then proceeded along these lines and it is clear that the matter was being approached absolutely from first principles.

Q. Among other things they deposit their pupae largely in holes in trees and not, as a rule, or not always, in places accessible to anything which might be destructive of them. We should be glad of any suggestions as to how to get the fly that way.

A. It seemed to me from the literature that I have read that attention has been more focused on the trypanosome than upon the habits of the fly itself. The fly, of course, is difficult to deal with for the very reason that it does not lay eggs or have larvae, but gives birth to a full-grown larva which immediately becomes a pupa and so it is to some extent protected. But the fly itself is an active thing. It has fairly complex sense organisms and instincts, and it seems to me possible that a method of dealing with the fly might have been obtained if a very close study of the fly itself had been made from a rather broad point of view.

We have, for instance, a fly in India which is extremely troublesome to fruit and by a purely chance discovery it was found that the flies over a large area could be attracted to one particular spot by the mere exposure of citronella oil. Further investigation has shown that it is due to the fact that the male recognises the female to some extent because she apparently gives off small quantities of this oil … It seemed to me that study directed to that point might possibly yield some method of trapping tse-tse flies on a large scale.

By trapping the male flies in this way, *Dacus persicae* was wiped out for all practical purposes. In the Professor's words: 'There are very few left.' The interview continued:

Q. Have you any suggestions with regard to finding and destroying the pupae?

A. I should imagine that practically nothing was possible. This is a case where local knowledge is everything, and that a person who had never seen a puparium or fly could really not express an opinion.

Q. If the flies are unable to get blood, or only a small proportion get it, would they disappear in the absence of breeding power?

A. I should say it was probable, but there is no statement you can make generally in entomology which is not contradicted somewhere or another. General statements in entomology are hopeless things to my mind. It seems probable... [You] have to study the insect itself. An observant study of the insect by itself is frequently barren of results, I think, unless it is worked in with study from the structural side – which is comparatively useless alone. By working systematically with the two things I think one can get some idea of what the insect's mind is doing, what it is thinking to some extent, what its instincts are, how far they are instinctive things, and how far purely reflex, and so on.

The really important thing is the minute and close study of one species. If I wanted to study an insect pest in India I used to go myself to the place where I could study it most easily, and the only thing to do is, as it were, to absorb oneself and steep oneself in the insect and try in a way to feel what the insect itself feels like, and so get an idea – it may be wrong; but you get eventually a sort of picture in your mind of what the insect is doing and why it does it. That is I think the root of the whole of successful entomology at the present time... One has to study the thing and try to find the weakest spot in the insect and go for it.

Q. Is there any likelihood of a parasite to pray upon *Glossina*?

A. Extremely improbable a direct parasite, but possibly something which preys on, catches and kills it. Possibly an insecticide found by local observation and study.

Q. What steps would you take?

A. I would go to the place, and I know no other method but to sit there and observe and study the insect, and think about it, and as it were steep oneself in the tse-tse fly until one began to see a way out. In my experience there nearly always is a way out; it may be something you dream about at night, or it may be something that comes to you from direct observation, but sooner or later if you think about the thing it seems to me you get a remedy. Frequently the remedy is impracticable on account of cost; that is the bugbear of this sort of thing; one has often to begin to think about cost, but that is the way I would proceed first, and after three, four, six months' experience of the insect itself I think one would be able to see how one could best proceed further.

Q. What kind of person would be willing to undertake such a study of the tse-tse fly?

A. In my experience the people who care for that sort of work are few, who thought and got at it in that sort of way. Personal characteristics are more important than training. In India I had over a hundred trained men, native staff, many with university degrees. I can think of only two who had that particular kind of brain organisation, or whatever it is.

In answer to a further question, he stated that, if the right man could be found, he would prefer one who had never read a word about *Glossina* and who would be approaching the question with an absolutely open mind.

Q. Have you studied the natural fungus parasites of insects much?

A. No. A locust fungus was sent to India from the Cape, and used without success in several parts of India. Some years later it was discovered it was the wrong fungus, the one which feeds on *dead* locusts.

Q. It is generally your view that a number of methods have not yet been tried?

A. I think so.

Q. From your knowledge of other insects, do you think it possible that any dip is likely to be discovered for cattle which would have a repellent effect on *Glossina*?

A. Extremely unlikely. In connection with a recent outbreak in New South Wales of a blow-fly which attacks sheep, I was asked whether I would go to Australia for a period of years to study it. The whole of the preliminary arrangements were made and we had planned out a

> line of campaign ... I have very little doubt that at the end of two to
> three years we should have got a dip which could be applied to sheep
> and would prevent the fly coming near the sheep.
> Q. Could a dip for sheep be used as an ointment for man?
> A. Possibly, but it would be so unpleasant and so impractical.
> Q. Why did you not go to Australia?
> A. The negotiations are not yet finished; that is the present position.
> Q. You think a good dip might be found?
> A. I think so.

It was, in fact, to be many years before any solution was found to
the problem of the tse-tse fly, not indeed during the lifetime of the
Professor. A more fruitful consultation, held at the same time, was
that which concerned the beams of Westminster Hall, many of which,
it had been discovered two years previously, were riddled with Death
Watch Beetle, some of them being actually hollow.

Westminster Hall is the one remaining part of the original Palace
of Westminster, the rest of which burnt down in 1834. It was built
initially by William Rufus, second of the Norman kings, in 1099, and
largely transformed, before 1299, by Richard II, last of the Plantagenet
kings. He caused the superb hammer-beam roof to be built, of oak
grown near Wadhurst in Sussex.

Traditionally, it was the scene of trials for high treason. Sir William
Wallace, the Scottish patriot, received his death sentence there in 1305;
Sir Thomas More received his in 1535 and Guy Fawkes his in 1606.
King Charles I was condemned to death there in 1649. More recently,
Warren Hastings was finally acquitted in the Hall in 1795, Queen
Caroline in 1820.

As a youth, a certain Frank Baines had obtained permission from
one of the old sailors, who used to report on and repair the roof, to
climb up their ladder to inspect the main collar beam. He walked
along this beam to its point of junction with the upper principal rafter
and succeeded in extracting a piece of wood which had been eaten
away in every direction, and looked like a sponge. Later, Mr Frank
Baines became chief of the Historic Buildings Branch of HM Office

of Works and made an official examination in 1911. His report, we learn from *The Times*,

> disclosed an appalling condition. It was only by a miracle that the roof had not fallen in; a catastrophe might happen at any moment. There was no dry rot, but the ravages of the death-watch beetle (*Xestobium tessellatum*), a little creature whose love-call has won for it its popular name, had turned the solid oak into a structure as spongy and friable as pumice stone. Many of the arches were feet out of alignment; joints were eaten through. Drastic steps had to be taken.

A scientific committee, consisting of architects, chemists and entomologists, began to sit. Many suggestions were made but all were rejected as impractical or impossible and, at the end of 1913, the committee dissolved without having come to any conclusion.

From *The Times* again:

> One of the members of the Committee, Mr. H.M. Lefroy… resolved, almost as a forlorn hope, to try to work out the problem with his pupils, and to find an answer that would fulfil the rigid conditions. The substance would have to destroy the insects and yet be non-poisonous, non-inflammable, and have the least possible odour. Its effects would have to be relatively permanent. The risk of introducing dry rot by the use of an aqueous solution would have to be avoided, and the golden colour of the wood be left unspoiled.

The Death Watch Beetle had not particularly been examined before. It was found living wild in both oak and willow trees and a fortunate chance discovered a stock of material for study. The adult could fly, but not very far. It was dark brown, about a quarter of an inch long. Its hard jaws had powerful muscles. It gnawed a shallow cavity in the wood and in this the female laid her eggs. These hatched in between two and four weeks and the grub then tunnelled inwards, eating the solid wood as it went. It fed for the whole summer, then rested during the winter. In the following summer it fed again and then turned into a chrysalis. Within three or four weeks it became a beetle. It rested as an immature adult before chomping its way out of the wood, usually in May, two years after being laid as an egg. Many beetles failed to eat through old wood as many dead bodies were discovered just below the surface of affected timbers.

In the words of Harold Maxwell-Lefroy:

> The grub, which does the tunnelling, has within its stomach an organism of a microscopic kind similar to a yeast, which is apparently a necessary fact in the digestion of the wood; it is probably deposited on the egg when it is laid, so that the grub becomes infected with what is apparently a necessary adjunct to its digestion; ... one might be able to sterilise the egg of its yeast without killing the egg, but still make life in the timber impossible for the grub.

Mr Frank Baines, quoted in *The Times* of the 22nd of May 1914, takes up the tale:

> All other methods of exterminating *Xestobium tessellatum* having failed, I called in the assistance of Professor Maxwell Lefroy, and he invented a spray, which is constituted thus – 50 per cent. tetrachlorethane, 6 per cent. cedarwood oil, 2 per cent. solvent soap, 2 per cent. paraffin wax, and 40 per cent. trichlorethylene. The first is a perfect insecticide, and is so dangerous that those who handle it must use gas masks – this was done on Saturday and Sunday. The cedarwood oil protects the wood against future attacks and the scent impregnates the timber and keeps the beetle away. The soap holds the oil and renders the wood non-inflammable, and the paraffin wax prevents chemical action. The trichlorethylene is a solvent and diluent – and is itself a feeble insecticide.

A steel frame was fitted to all the timbers in the roof, invisible from below, but nonetheless regarded as a great aesthetic crime at the time. The original beams were treated against the beetle, were patched and repaired with wood from the Wadhurst forest, but were not removed or replaced. The work, which began in 1914, was not to be completed for seven years.

On the 14th of March 1921, *The Times* carried this report:

> After many trials, cedar wood oil, in quantities so small that it was innocuous to the human nostril, was found extremely distasteful to beetles and grubs. Solid paraffin suggested itself as a medium almost indestructible when

exposed to London air and smoke, and in a thin layer so transparent as not to obscure the colour of the surface to which it was applied. The liquid known as di-chlora-benzine provided a solvent which gave penetrating power, and was almost absolutely uninflammable and non-poisonous as a vapour. The formula was 92 per cent. of the solvent, 3 per cent. of soap, 3 per cent. of paraffin wax, and 2 per cent. of cedar wood oil. This is sprayed on every surface as it is exposed, on every separated piece of wood, old or new, and again on the finished surface when the reassembling has been done and the steel fitted in. The di-chlora-benzine slowly evaporates, leaving behind a transparent film of wax impregnated with the oil. The newly treated wood undoubtedly has an odour, and the atmosphere of the Hall recalls that of a 'doping' room of an aeroplane factory. But the wood that has been treated for some time gives off no appreciable scent, and has lost none of its golden colour. The work has been in progress for several years, and so far the treatment seems to be completely effective.

It was this second mixture that was most widely used, brushed on or sprayed, as it was as effective as the first one but non-poisonous. While the work went on, the Professor modified the liquid to make it simpler, cheaper and even more effective. The final recipe was 50 per cent dichlorobenzene, 47 per cent mineral oil and 3 per cent barium oleate.

A magnificent building, of great historical importance and enormous architectural value, had been saved, with all its unique, irreplaceable carvings. A beetle had been studied, its grubs in all probability already present in the original timbers, and a liquid invented which sealed its death-warrant. For his work at Westminster Hall, Mr Frank Baines was offered, and accepted, a knighthood. If Professor Maxwell-Lefroy was offered one at the same time – and there is a legend in the family to this effect – then either the offer was not actually made or else he politely refused it.

In May 1914, the first volume of *Annals of Applied Biology*, the official organ of the Association of Economic Biologists, was published, with an editorial by Harold Maxwell-Lefroy.

The Association was founded ten years ago and commences herewith the publication of a journal devoted to the special interests of its members. During this period its scope has broadened, and the *Annals* is intended to cover the ground in applied biology which is not now covered by specialist journals such as those dealing with agricultural sciences, parasitology, genetics and medical science … It is now intended to deal with other branches of applied biology, and we are glad to be able to issue in our first number a wide range of papers, which will soon become still wider. All papers which bear on the scientific problems of applied biology will be welcome; we have no place for pure systematic work which is amply provided for elsewhere …

Few people realise how great is the progress made in applied biology in the overseas Dominions in the last twenty years and how vital to the success of all tropical industries is the work that is being done in applied biology; it has become evident in regard to medicine, but it is less realised in agriculture, horticulture, animal breeding and other industries in which investors at home are interested. Nevertheless, such industries depend for their continued prosperity more and more on research in biology and the application of its results.

If large problems in which technical knowledge is required, are settled without the technical expert being seriously consulted … it is the fault not of the official mind nor the man in the street, but of applied biologists themselves.

At the recent physio-pathological Congress in Rome the technical experts were outnumbered by the diplomats though the questions were admittedly technical.

It was once a custom in India to appoint a medical officer to any scientific post, simply because science was so vague a conception to the senior official educated in the classics, that he could not conceive of subdivisions in science.

The first volume contained eight articles, one of which was an account, by R.H. Deakin, of 'The caterpillars attacking the oaks of Richmond Park, with an account of an experiment spraying with lead chromate'. He had worked under the Professor's guidance and, in the article, thanked him for his advice. He referred also to the twenty students from Imperial College who had helped with the spraying. Mr Deakin was by then working in East Africa.

There was an impressive list of other editors, professors from the Universities of Birmingham, Manchester (Dr A.D. Imms), Liverpool and Leeds; one from the Imperial Institute and one more from Imperial College; one from the National Fruit and Cider Institute in Bristol and one, Mr F.J. Chittenden, from the Royal Horticultural Society's Gardens at Wisley. He contributed an article on 'Pollination in Orchards' to the first issue.

It was possibly as a result of this connection that the Professor became part-time honorary entomologist at Wisley, a sandy-soiled garden in Surrey, presented by Sir Thomas Hanbury to the Royal Horticultural Society in 1903. In 1914, Mr Chittenden, who was later to edit the Royal Horticultural Society's *Dictionary of Gardening*, became Director of the laboratory there, and head of the School of Horticulture. He is described as 'temperate to the point of austerity', with 'remarkable powers of self-control', 'iron nerves and he apparently knew no fear'. Mr George Fox Wilson became the Professor's practical assistant.

A cutting remains from an unidentified newspaper of the time. Under the heading 'Enquiry' it says:

> The Shot Borer Beetle. Professor Lefroy, Entomologist to the Royal Horticultural Society, will be obliged if growers of fruit in Surrey or neighbouring counties whose trees are infested with the Shot Borer Beetle (*Xyleborus dispar*) will communicate with him at the R.H.S. Gardens, Wisley, Ripley, Surrey. He desires particularly to learn whether there are in the neighbourhood indicated any considerable attacks of the pest.

Whether there were any replies to this or not we do not know. We do know that he must have spent time that summer carefully observing the Turnip Flea Beetle, *Phyllotreta consobrima*, and then devising a trap for it. They were said to 'jump nimbly like fleas'.

It is a small, bluish beetle, a well-known enemy of turnips, swedes, cabbages and other members of the family *Cruciferae*. In fine sunny weather it can be seen sitting on the little seedling plants eating round holes in the leaves. Its principal targets are the two leaves of the plant as it springs out of the ground. Damage to these, on which the plant entirely depends at that stage, can seriously set back its development, or even kill it completely.

The Wisley Trap, a kind of sledge invented by Professor Lefroy, was described in some detail in the *Gardener's Chronicle* of the 5th of September 1914.

To a frame made of six pieces of half inch deal 20 in. long, two pieces of this board (20 in. by 5 in.) are fixed so as to slope outwards and upwards, on the sides of the frame. These sloping boards are held apart by a cross bar and an end piece, so as to have four clear inches between them at the bottom. The two bottom outer pieces of the frame are made ½ in. deeper than the inner pieces, the whole trap riding on the outer pair as a sledge on runners. The ends are rounded off to allow of the free running of the 'sledge'. The sloping boards, the end pieces facing them, and the cross piece between them are greased. From the cross bar between the sloping pieces hangs a loop of stout string, and for drawing the sledge strings four feet long are attached to the front top corners.

If the trap is drawn along each row of Turnips so that the young plants pass under the cross bar and are brushed by the string loop, the beetles leap up and alight on the sticky boards. There they perish. If made of deal this apparatus is so light that a child can draw it along the rows; it is best for two persons to draw the trap and for them to walk a few feet away on each side so that the beetles are not disturbed until the sticky boards reach them. If two persons are not available, one can work the trap, drawing it with outstretched arm, and walking so that the shadow falls on rows already done.

Satisfactory sticky substances include: Messrs. Wood and Son's Currant Gall Mite Grease and Smearing Grease (1s.3d a tin); The S.P. Charges Co., St. Helens, 'Morlar' Hop Wash (1s. a tin).

This little device was designed to deal with the hordes of flea beetles on the Turnips at Wisley. It works so pleasantly and there is such a charm in mopping up the flea beetles that the above description is published. The method may no doubt be adapted to large cultivation by making a number of sledge traps in series so as to do, say, five rows at once; but the present pattern is intended for garden use.

Those who wish to purchase traps can obtain them from Messrs. Wood and Son, North British Wharf, Wood Green, N., carriage paid for 3s.6d. The traps may also be obtained, carriage forward, from Mr. Paddle, 26, Loring Road, Isleworth, at 2s.3d, and from Messrs. Walker and Sons, London Road, Isleworth, at 2s.6d.

But the stable, secure world that is conjured up by this idyllic scene – two children trapping Turnip Beetles on a sunny afternoon, with a sledge trap made, one must suppose, by one of two local carpenters in Isleworth to the Professor's design – had already vanished.

On the 28th of June, the Archduke Franz Ferdinand, heir to the throne of Austria-Hungary, and his morganatic wife, were shot dead by a Bosnian student. The incident occurred in Sarajevo, capital of a Bosnia that was part of the Austro-Hungarian Empire. He sought, and was granted, asylum in Serbia. It was suspected in Vienna that this was part of a well-organised Serbian plot, although the assassin was in fact a member of the Black Hand, a Bosnian underground movement. His extradition was demanded of Serbia by Austria and an ultimatum was issued. It expired. A month after the incident, Austria declared war on Serbia. Russia, Serbia's ally, came to her aid, mobilising along her southern front.

On the 1st of August Germany, allied to Austria, declared war on Russia. Two days later, on the day that the first ship sailed through the Panama Canal, Germany declared war on France, allied to Russia. Kaiser Wilhelm II demanded free passage for his troops through Belgium, to invade France more easily, but this was denied. On the 4th of August the Germans invaded Belgium and the United Kingdom, guarantor of Belgium's borders since 1831, declared war on Germany.

A British Expeditionary Force set off immediately, intending to prevent the Germans over-running France, and the four nations remained locked in conflict, in trenches and dugouts, advancing, retiring, going over the top, going under the wire, troubled by flies and lice, by rats and by ankle-deep mud as much as by shell-fire, machine-gun and rifle bullets and by poison gas, for more than four years. A notable battle was fought at Cambrai, original home of Antoine l'Offroy.

It was a clash of enormous forces.

The Central Alliance, or the Central Powers, the Empires of Germany and of Austro-Hungary, were joined, in 1915, by the Turkish, or Ottoman, Empire and by the Kingdom of Bulgaria.

The Allies, or the Entente, the United Kingdom with its Dominions and Colonies and its Indian Empire, the French Republic and the Kingdom of Belgium, both with large colonial empires, and the Russian Empire, were joined by the Empire of Japan almost immediately, and before the end of November by the Republic of Portugal and its large overseas possessions. The independent Kingdom of Italy joined the Allies in 1915, and that of Rumania in 1916. In 1917 the United States of America and of Brazil, both republics, joined the Entente.

The Kingdoms of Holland and Denmark contrived to remain neutral.

Apart from the stalemate war in Flanders, the fighting took place principally in Serbia and the Balkans, especially on the border of Greece with Turkey, at Salonika, Gallipoli and the Dardanelles; in Mesopotamia, now Iraq, then an important part of the Ottoman Empire; and in various parts of Africa, wherever the Germans had established colonies.

The war was also fiercely fought at sea, in the Pacific and Indian Oceans, in the North and the South Atlantic, in the Mediterranean and in the North Sea, then known as the German Ocean.

Enormous losses of life were sustained on all sides and hostilities finally ceased on the eleventh day of the eleventh month of 1918, at eleven o'clock in the morning.

CHAPTER XIV

The Professor volunteered for military service, but he was turned down on medical grounds. It is not known precisely what was wrong. He was by now thirty-seven years old, and ten years spent in the tropics at that time cannot have improved the health of anyone, particularly not of anyone who approached his work with what is described as 'daemonic energy'. He now devoted those energies to alleviating the lot of the British troops, wherever they might be, concentrating especially on the ultimate extermination of body lice and flies.

His brief connection with the Royal Horticultural Society had already produced two pamphlets, which were now published: 'On keeping fruit-trees clean' and 'On keeping orchards clean'. The points principally made were that injurious insects tended to winter in the grass or in rotting fruit, and that the former should be cut as low as possible – the trees should ideally be grown in open ground – and the latter removed entirely. Dead wood should be cut out and a grease band fixed around each tree.

He also pointed out that various insects, twenty-one species in all, which attacked fruit trees, also fed on hawthorn, sloe, willow and sallow, poplar and oak, cotoneaster and roses, and that these plants should not be grown anywhere near an orchard. He advised what is called a 'winter wash' and also a summer spraying, various kinds of which were still being tested. The report of the RHS Council for 1915 records that he was still researching into 'The Prevention of White Fly and Scale'.

On the 2nd of February 1915, *The Times* published his letter:

Pediculus and Phthirius

The plague of lice is not the least of the hardships of war, and I ask space to point out that a simple remedy exists which kills the lice and confers immunity for a time. Unlike petrol, benzine, etc. it is non-inflammable; it is harmless, but has a distinct smell. The authorities are aware of it and are testing it; as some delay must occur in making it available, and as a shilling purchases enough for more than one person I shall be glad to give information to any who desire to send some to relatives or friends at the front or in this country.

There were twenty shillings in a pound.

Lice, both the body louse and the crab louse, emerge fully active from the egg. These are laid attached to hair on all parts of the body and on clothing, particularly in the seams. After hatching, they go through several moults before achieving maturity, sucking the blood of their host and transmitting both typhus and what was then known as 'trench fever'. The 'simple remedy' referred to was in all probability Vermijelli, certainly made up to the Professor's recipe, which was to come into official use later.

Two replies to this letter still exist. While we cannot know what reply was sent to them, they do give a very vivid picture of the problem. The first is dated the 3rd of February 1915 from 'Heatherside, Worplesdon, Surrey':

Professor H.M. Lefroy,

Dear Sir

I read your letter in yesterday's 'Times' with great interest, and as I may shortly be proceeding to tropical Africa, as Intelligence Officer, with a force which Col. Driscoll has been called upon by the War Office to raise immediately, I should be extremely obliged if you will let me know what exactly the remedy is against insects to which you refer in your article, for if this expedition actually comes off, our men will be sorely troubled, not only by lice, sandflies and mosquitoes, but also by jigger fleas, and ticks. A pinch of your remedy sprinkled in their socks, might preserve them from jigger fleas, which are very troublesome in the coast regions of British and German East Africa.

Believe me, yours very truly

F.C. Selous.

The second, written on mourning paper with a black band quarter of an inch deep all the way round, is addressed from 'Hampton Court Palace, Middlesex':

Dear Sir

Thank you for sending me the 'Pediculus' recipe. I understand from military authorities, that they supply the men with stuff to kill the *live* vermin but that the *eggs* are the difficulty, they exist in millions in their clothing, boiling water is quite ineffectual, & so far nothing has been found to destroy the eggs. Would *your* prescription kill the eggs? My interest in the soldiers being relieved from the torment must be my excuse for writing again.

Faithfully yours,

L. Wolseley.

6.2.15

This was Louisa, Lady Wolseley, whose husband, the famous Sir Garnet, later Viscount, Wolseley, had died in 1913.

A third letter, written by Dr Kenneth M. Smith, CBE, FRS, in March 1980, is also of interest here.

I was a student at Imperial College in South Kensington in 1911 and on my return from the Western Front in 1915, I studied entomology under Maxwell Lefroy and took my diploma in entomology (D.I.C.) under him. At that time I think I was his only student and got to know him well. He was working on some antidote to the body louse which was the scourge of soldiers in France, it also carried 'trench fever'. Lefroy managed to concoct a horrible salve called 'Vermijelly' – whether it ever got into general use I don't know. He was also very interested in controlling the house fly and I remember the room, with about 12 bunsen burners going at full blast, where he bred his houseflies.

The Professor's son offers this recollection:

> And there was Vermigelli but I'm not sure what it was for. Dark brown. I
> suppose somebody must have made it. I can't think what it was made *of*.
> But it wasn't good to eat and didn't smell so we soon lost interest.

While officialdom conducted its tests, the Professor turned his
attention to the Insect House at the Zoo, where things had been
happening, some disastrous, some not. The Professor exercised his
Fellow's privilege by inviting his wife, and his brother Jack and his
wife, to lunch at the Zoo, the latter in particular enjoying these
occasions, delighting in her brother-in-law's enthusiasms and his
wonderfully clear explanations about everything that went on in the
Insect House.

But a report of the 23rd of March tells us that the Head Keeper has
died and has not been replaced, everyone being at the War. They were
now attempting to keep alive, and in good condition, only the existing
inmates. They were not looking for any new residents.

Large numbers of leaf insects, however, had actually vanished,
eaten, it was supposed, by a spider which had also vanished, though
it was later discovered lurking behind a panel. Among the *Mantidae*,
the Praying Mantises, many full-grown specimens had in fact died as
a result of being nibbled by their fellow lodgers. While they had not
all died, they had all been nibbled.

A rare beetle, discovered at the Millwall Docks, feeding on fungi
to be found on decaying logs, had been offered asylum. A Giant
Ground Beetle, despatched from Trinidad, arrived alone, having eaten
all his fellow-travellers on the voyage. Death Watch Beetles had been
discovered in an oak tree, offering useful material for testing and study,
the extermination of their counterparts in Westminster Hall being in
view; but of the five Six-spotted Ground Beetles received from India in
July 1914 only one remained alive.

None of these insects offered any threat to humanity, nor were they
involved in the war effort. All other activities were now suspended in

an attempt to exterminate the common housefly, *Musca domestica*, which was making existence even more intolerable for the troops on the Western Front. Its life history was known but methods of controlling it were not; and it was to assume the proportions of an obsession in the Professor's life.

Flies breed principally in the summer months; but in warm stables, for instance, in restaurants or in large kitchens, they could do so all the year round. A single fly might lay between a hundred and a hundred and fifty eggs at a time, and these would hatch within twenty-four hours. A fly could become a grandparent in about three weeks.

The larvae, known as maggots, bury themselves before pupating. Middens, manure heaps, mounds of decaying rubbish of various kinds, are a favourite place for this. The flies emerge, sexually mature within a week or ten days, able to lay eggs within four days of mating. The whole cycle can be completed within ten days, in three weeks at most.

When it is considered that all the transport in Flanders and in France was drawn by horses or mules, that officers rode horses, frequently their own, that there were still fully mounted cavalry regiments and that there were several hundred thousand men engaged in the hostilities, the scale of the plague can easily be imagined.

From *Indian Insect Life*:

They breed in decaying refuse of all sorts, especially dung, and it will often be found that plagues of flies are due to the near presence of stables and cease as soon as measures are taken either to remove the stable refuse daily, or to protect it from flies with a layer of lime, by copiously sprinkling it every day with crude-oil emulsion,... or by keeping it thoroughly soaked with water, or in fly-proof bins or pits. The heaps of decaying vegetable stuff near the bungalow, so often seen on indigo-planters' estates, are one of the main causes of the plagues of flies from which they periodically suffer... the insects carry on their feet and other parts of the body traces of filthy matter on which they are accustomed to sit and suck, and are liable to infect our food and milk with the germs of stomach-diseases derived from this filth.

The Professor suggested that an exhibition should be arranged to illustrate the dangers to health presented by blowflies, bluebottles and houseflies, and that methods of combating them should be explained. This was agreed and he was released from his other duties by Imperial College and by the Royal Horticultural Society, both of whom gave their enthusiastic support.

The horticultural stations at Swanley, in Kent, and Reading, the Army authorities and the Cooper Research Laboratory at Berkhamsted – founded six or seven years previously for precisely this kind of research – all offered facilities and the exhibition opened in May 1915, at the Zoological Society's Gardens in Regent's Park.

In 1937 Sir Peter Chalmers Mitchell, later to found the Whipsnade Zoo, but by then Secretary of the Zoological Society, wrote in his book *My Fill of Days*:

> Maxwell Lefroy was one of the most resourceful experimentalists I have ever known. I was a little doubtful about the time and trouble he was giving to the search for baits specifically attractive to different kinds of flies, as I thought that most kinds of decaying matter were equally attractive. But he assured me that there was a marked preference for special breeding-grounds and that he would undertake to prepare three separate baits for three species of flies, all very rare in London, and expose these in the Gardens, and find the named species within a few days. He caught the flies.

The Times of the 13th of May carried this report:

> Anti-fly exhibition.
>
> The exhibition organized by Professor Maxwell-Lefroy is designed not only to teach householders how to keep the home clear of flies but as a source of information for public health authorities in planning anti-fly campaigns. Open to the public, 10 a.m. till noon. Open to doctors, nurses, public health and sanitary staffs in the afternoon.
>
> The exhibition will continue all through the summer if necessary. It is in a room in the Superintendent's House, and includes American fly-traps, with home modifications, fly bats, sprays and syringes, and various forms of bait, poison and insecticides. An excellent pamphlet is available from Miss E. Chick, Chestergate, Ealing W.

The Professor pointed out that it was most desirable to find treatment for manure heaps as the present shortage of manpower meant delays in moving them. If money was available research could be undertaken into ways of dealing with manure, the most prolific breeding-ground for flies, and this was most necessary. At present the only method was the American one, with borax, but the cost of this made it impracticable.

Mr. Boland will today ask the President of the local Government Board in the House of Commons what steps are being taken to inform the public of the fly peril under existing war-time conditions.

According to *Hansard* of the 13th of May, Mr Boland did so. Mr Herbert Samuel replied that seven reports had been issued and several circular letters had been sent out. Another was about to be issued. The War Office was co-operating with his Board in this and other matters affecting the health of the civil and military populations.

> A number of local authorities have issued posters and leaflets on this subject. I am considering the preparation and issue by the Local Government Board of a series of model leaflets on this and other health subjects, which local authorities could use if they so desired. I hardly think it necessary to appoint a committee.

Asked by Lord Robert Cecil whether any communication had taken place between the English and French authorities on this point, Mr Samuel replied: 'Not so far as I am aware.'

A laconic press cutting still exists, of unknown provenance, under the title 'Kill That Fly!' 'Professor Maxwell Lefroy is about to initiate another campaign against the fly by means of a public lecture at the Zoo. The agitation against this homely pest grows fiercer year by year, but the fly seems to flourish all the same.'

The lecture was given at the beginning of June 'as part of the Zoological Society's campaign against flies'. In it, he mentioned that a letter to *The Times* had produced 10,000 replies in four months and, for lack of other evidence, we may assume that it was the letter on the subject of body lice, *Pediculus* and *Phthirius*.

The common housefly, he said in his lecture, could produce nine hundred eggs in a lifetime, and the life of one generation was three weeks. The Blow Fly, in a much longer life, produced six hundred eggs. The Lesser Horse Fly did not settle on human food and therefore was less dangerous, but its appearance was a warning that the common housefly, that 'winged and wandering bundle of bacteria', was breeding somewhere near.

Flies needed moist conditions for their larvae; dry material produced no flies. Flies disliked darkness. Municipal and other tips should be treated with chloride of lime; the burning of all kinds of refuse was recommended as were a number of other methods, involving oil, borax, slaked lime and formalin. Flies also avoid shade. Milk, water, food and fruit, for instance, should all be covered and kept in fly-screened larders or meat safes.

The exhibition at the Zoo continued throughout the summer, drawing enormous crowds to whom a great deal of this information was previously unknown.

The Professor turned some of the outbuildings at Acton Lodge into a fly-farm.

> I remember odd happenings in a range of barn-like buildings but was told to keep out. And I remember the room, with about twelve Bunsen burners going full blast, where Father bred his houseflies.

On the 6th of July, *The Times* reported: 'The National League for Physical Education and Improvement met yesterday at the Mansion House to inaugurate a campaign to prevent the spread of epidemics by insects in wartime.'

Sir Frederick Treves, the surgeon who performed the appendectomy on King Edward VII, saving his life, and who was instrumental in founding the International Red Cross, should have attended this meeting. Being unwell, he wrote instead, to *The Times*: 'In South Africa during the war there more casualties were due to flies than to bullets. In France the presence of so many unburied dead makes the fly question a very serious one.'

He went on to say that the present difficult and distressing conditions in Alexandria, in Egypt, were largely due to the vast numbers of cavalry horse lines near the town, and he also remarked on the fact that a recent outbreak of typhus in Ireland had been traced to an importation of infested clothing from Glasgow.

'Professor Lefroy dealt chiefly with the horsefly,' said *The Times*.

It carried summer diarrhoea from child to child and killed between five thousand and fifteen thousand children annually. It also carried typhoid and cholera. 'This is going to be a fly year', he said. He protested that open manure heaps were a danger and a scandal. 'We must educate people, we must insist on cleanliness, especially in the home.'

The point was also made that powers should be obtained to control the exposure of food in shops, markets and restaurants. Flies had access to this food. The only food concerning which special powers existed was ice cream.

The *Daily Mail*, on Saturday the 31st of July 1915, carried a long article under the title:

THE FLY MAGNET
How To Kill The Pest Born and Unborn
Professor's Sure Traps.

Behind an old house covered with creepers at New Brentford, Middlesex, is an experimental 'Fly Farm' – the first of its kind.

The Perfect Bait

It is casein, brown sugar and water mixed in equal parts. This mixture must be left to stand for 24 hours or so before a fly will take much notice of it. Then some slight change sets in, due no doubt to fermentation, and from that moment he will not be kept away. Some subtle smell about the mixture appeals to house-fly taste and he surges anxiously and innocently round the bottle.

After some hours the girl assistant comes along with a drop of ether on a rag, drops it in the cone of the trap, and puts a glass slab to keep in the fumes till the flies are stupefied. Then they are counted. From 10a.m. on the 29th to 10 a.m. the following morning the trap so baited caught more than 600 flies... Casein, which is the chief solid that goes to the making of milk, can be had for 45s. a hundredweight, or 5d. a pound. It has proved the best and cheapest fly bait of many hundreds that Professor Maxwell

Lefroy has tried, and he has gone into the business on scientific lines, using during his four months' experiments every kind of thing from chemicals to beer and bananas.

… It has been noticed that house flies never breed in a house, but go out generally to the nearest manure heap, each to lay her 900 eggs. They burrow into the manure and lay, generally about six or nine inches from the surface. After passing through the maggot and chrysalis stage the young flies emerge. A third of a bucketful of this sub-surface manure yielded 218 flies. On this basis a quite small manure heap would yield a quarter of a million flies.

But if it were 'dressed' with the cheap and simple dressing Professor Maxwell Lefroy has discovered not a fly would come to life. This dressing is just plain earth or sand mixed with 'green oil', a cheap oil distilled from tar. One gallon of this oil, costing 1s., mixed with 40 gallons (thirteen bucketfuls) of earth will make a dressing sufficient to cover a manure heap of 80 square feet in area.

For these experiments, the results of which should be of first importance in the promotion of public health, ways and means were found by the Zoological Society of London and its secretary, Dr. Chalmers Mitchell.

The article was accompanied by a photograph of the Professor examining his 'catch' in a large glass jar, unfortunately no longer in existence.

A pamphlet issued by the Zoological Society in August charted the success of the exhibition held earlier in the year and of all the lectures inspired by it.

It was soon found that there were questions on which more knowledge was required. The Imperial College of Science joined in the investigation; a staff of assistants was enrolled; the Local Government Board made a grant towards expenses, and the Zoological Society and Mr. Otto Beit, FZS, also provided funds. Facilities were given at the military station at Woolwich, by the Royal Horticultural Society at Wisley, at the Horticultural College at Swanley, at University College, Reading and much experimental work was done in the Zoological Gardens.

But for the Professor his work on the fly menace was temporarily over. The Royal Horticultural Society's Report for 1915 puts it very nicely.

In the spring of the year the Society's Entomologist, Professor Maxwell Lefroy, M.A., was temporarily released from his duties at Wisley to enable him to undertake, on behalf of the War Office, an investigation into the means of destroying the eggs and larvae of flies, with the object of preventing outbreaks of disease. His investigations proved to be of much value, and a summary of them will be published in the *Journal*. Later in the year he was urgently requested by the Secretary of State to proceed to India, in order to undertake another entomological investigation for the Government. The Council felt that the acceptance by Professor Lefroy of this appointment, entailing absence from England till January 1917 at least, rendered the holding of his Wisley appointment impossible, and his resignation was accordingly accepted, though with the greatest regret.

It continued:

With the appointment of Professor Lefroy as Entomologist to the Society, relations were established between the Society and the Imperial College of Science. Although Professor Lefroy was compelled to relinquish his appointment in November these relations remain, and the prime object which they were designed to fulfil, namely, the establishment of a National Station for Research in Entomology at Wisley, will be pursued.

This new entomological investigation was into the condition of the silk industry in India, into its present state and all the possibilities that could be found for its extension; and it is clear that this was considered to be of the greatest possible importance.

The matter was first put to the Secretary of State for India, Mr Austen Chamberlain, by the Government of India at the end of September. They informed him that the industry begun by the late Mr Tata was flourishing, in Mysore, and that opportunities existed for it to be extended to other parts of India. The Salvation Army, in particular, already had twenty-three centres, where they had trained several hundred reelers, spinners, weavers and silkworm growers. They suggested Harold Maxwell-Lefroy as being the best possible person to undertake the enquiry, studying conditions at the silk centres all over India and then continuing to Indo-China and Japan. A salary of up to £1,750 a year was proposed for twelve months and his arrival was requested, if possible, in November.

On the 4th of November, Imperial College was asked to release him and on the same day the Under Secretary of State, Lord Islington, put the proposal to the Professor formally. On the 5th of November he accepted and he and his wife left for India on the 12th. In view of the danger from German submarines, they travelled across France and sailed from Marseilles, on the SS *Salsette*, on the 13th of November.

On the 15th of November, Imperial College agreed to release him until December of the next year, and on the 1st of December 1915, as Imperial Silk Specialist, he landed in Bombay. Left on his own 'at home', their son offers this wry recollection:

I went to prep school, Ladycross, Seaford, when my parents went off to India. It closed down a few years ago. I stayed with various aunts. I used to spend my holidays with them. There was a distressing scene on one occasion when no less than two aunts turned up to collect me at Victoria. One grabbed me by one arm and the other grabbed me by the other but the Lefroy aunt was the stronger and so I went with her. But they didn't forget me. Or any rate mother didn't. I used to get food parcels at my prep school. The trouble was I never got them. The headmaster grabbed them and doled them all out.

CHAPTER XV

A press communiqué on the 30th of November announced the Professor's appointment as Silk Specialist, specifically to enquire into the possibility of reviving the Indian silk industry. He and his wife went straight to Delhi where, on the 4th of December, there was a high-level Silk Conference.

Its purpose was principally to discuss the Professor's itinerary. He had already drawn up his own proposals. He would begin at once with a visit to the Salvation Army farms in Simla and then go on to Bengal. He would spend December and January with the Salvation Army in Bengal and in the United Provinces, but would attend the Board of Agriculture meeting at Pusa in February. Here he hoped to meet the Directors of Agriculture from the Punjab and Bombay and, possibly, Burma and arrange tours of their provinces with them. He would spend the rest of February in Assam and go on to the Punjab and Bombay in March.

The Hon. Mr C.H.A. Hill, a member of the Viceroy's Council, suggested that it would be better to visit Bombay first and this was agreed.

The Professor then proposed going to Kashmir in April, spending May and June in Japan and July and August in French Indo-China on his way back. He would visit South India in September and continue to Burma, returning to India in October.

The question of his associate was discussed and a Salvation Army expert was proposed. The Professor, however, is recorded as saying that the person concerned had been of no use as Sericulture Assistant at Pusa, and the proposal was withdrawn. The Professor would receive, as a matter of course, all possible assistance on his travels.

His 'establishment' consisted of a clerk in the eighth grade, Babu Dwarka Das, who was to receive 100 rupees a month, and two peons, at ten rupees a month each. On the 3rd of January the Professor, from Pusa, requested an increase in their 'halting allowance' – money required for overnight, or longer, stays. He asked ten rupees for himself – from which we may guess that his wife was travelling with him – three rupees for his clerk and four annas each for his peons.

In March, Government agreed to two rupees for the clerk and four annas for the peons, but he was sternly told that his own allowance had to remain within the Civil Service regulations. He had been appointed directly by the Government of India.

On the 24th of February, Mr E.C. Ansorge, an Officiating Joint Magistrate and Deputy Collector in Bihar and Orissa, was instructed to join the Professor in Calcutta as soon as possible after the 1st of March and they would continue their travels together. Mr Ansorge had already arranged for some Eri silk to be sold in London and it had done well; but his principal interest was in the weavers' conditions of work.

On the 26th of February the Professor telegraphed to the Government of India that he was cancelling his passage to Japan and altering his programme; it appears that he wished to go sooner to Japan than he had intended. Mr Ansorge was then requested to join him in Poona, a military station in the hills behind Bombay, on the 7th of March.

The *Report on an Inquiry into the Silk Industry in India*, by H.M. Lefroy and E.C. Ansorge, was published in three volumes in 1917, in Calcutta. It is a completely comprehensive document, lucid and informative, and the basis on which the Indian silk industry was gradually to revive. Although, in February 1919, the Professor was still comparing, in a lecture, how much the French had done for the silk industry in their colonies – a great deal – with the performance of the British in theirs – almost negligible – the revival had already begun, and was to continue throughout the 1920s, gradually attaining a momentum that it retains to this day.

Volume I of the *Report* is in eight parts.

Part I is about the existing industry in India, confined to Bengal, Mysore and Madras, Kashmir and Jammu, the Punjab, Assam and Burma. It contains practical suggestions as to how the conditions, and therefore the output, could be improved.

Part II is concerned with new areas for silk production, the climate and soil required, and, in particular, the population. This had to be large and at least semi-skilled. The experimental stations at Indore, Gwalior and Travancore are discussed and the conclusion is that sericulture is worth the attempt where the basic conditions appear to be right.

Part III is purely technical: the growing of mulberry trees, the rearing of silkworms and the various types of silkworm.

Part IV is largely about the training required to produce skilled workers. As before, the lack of trained experts is lamented, but the methods of training are here criticised, in particular those of the Salvation Army. 'To develop sericulture you must go to the people themselves, not expect the people to come to the schools.' It is nevertheless suggested that the training could begin in primary school.

Part V deals with the various kinds of wild silk, and the areas where they are produced. Eri silk, it is noted here, is the only kind of silk that can be wound off the cocoon without killing the insect inside it. It is therefore the only kind of silk that can be worn by the strict Hindu, whose clothes are normally made of cotton.

Part VI is about the different kinds of silk process. In particular, it advocates more home weaving in India, as in Japan.

Part VII discusses the silk industry in various areas, differences in method and in the kind of cloth produced, with several illuminating suggestions.

Part VIII contains many practical recommendations for the development of the industry in all its aspects. Improved processes are required and new designs; an efficient commercial organisation is needed. It is in fact what would today be described as a 'blueprint' for the entire silk industry, from the silkworm itself to the marketing of the finished product.

The second volume of the *Report* consists principally of statistics, and the third volume of Appendices to Volume I. Like *Indian Insect Life*, it is a monumental work, thorough, far-sighted and clear, containing just about all the information then available on the subject of making silk.

We must suppose that the tour of India continued along the lines originally discussed. On the 25th of March, the Professor telegraphed to Government from Lahore: 'Not taking clerk to Japan. Have found competent Indian trained in Japan, China and Indo-China who could come for same pay and travel allowance. Can I arrange?'

On the 15th of April, Government agreed.

But on the 17th of April, Government telegraphed the Professor, by then in Bangalore:

Military authorities applying for your services for fly and vermin destruction in Mesopotamia. Do you consider Beeson (Forest Zoologist) in all respects qualified to deal with this matter and if so has he equal facilities with you for operating by your methods and would it be desirable for you to meet Beeson if latter is accepted?

To which the Professor replied, by return:

Beeson better than no entomologist but without experience or my facilities. If Beeson accepted necessary he meet me before going. Proper course send both, let me return when Beeson qualified. Useless sending anyone unless supply necessary chemicals and appliances can be arranged. Given this flies and vermin can be destroyed.

On the 19th of April, in answer to a further telegram about the supply of chemicals and other necessary appliances, the Professor telegraphed:

Some chemicals required can be got in India, some only in London. My point is that if there is delay in obtaining what may be required no work will be possible. Cannot tell amount required till I get there but can indicate kinds advisable. Order 1,000 gallons fly spray and 1,000 sprayers from Heppell, 164 Piccadilly, or through War Office as this not obtainable here. Rest can be got in India.

On the 26th of April, Government again telegraphed: 'Medical Stores Depot, Bombay, has formula for your fly spray and can arrange sprayers. Your services and Beeson's are being placed at disposal of military authorities and you will receive instructions from the Director of Medical Services.'

With effect from the 23rd of April, the Professor became Acting Lieutenant Colonel at 1,875 rupees per month, and Mr C.F.C. Beeson Acting Captain at 650 rupees. They received a special allowance of five rupees a day for the period of their absence from India and an allowance of 450 rupees for uniforms and camp equipment; and, in July, the Secretary of State in London was asked to advise that the Professor's plans to visit Japan and Indo-China were abandoned.

The campaign in Mesopotamia was principally fought, on behalf of the Allies, by the Indian Army. A survivor of this campaign wrote, in 1992: 'The soldiers then needed three hands to enable them to eat. One to hold the *chupatti*, one to clear a path to the mouth and a third to prevent the mouth from being invaded – by descendants of the flies which plagued the armies of Genghis Khan!'

The Commander-in-Chief of the Indian Army, Sir Beauchamp Duff, was stationed in Simla and the campaign was planned from there. He was also, of course, the Military Advisor on the Viceroy's Council, a situation which Lord Curzon had tried to prevent and over which he had resigned ten years before.

Sir Beauchamp did not actually approach the scene of hostilities any more nearly than Bombay, but Lieutenant Colonel Maxwell-Lefroy did. His account of his attachment in Mesopotamia was published shortly afterwards by the *Agricultural Journal of India*.

There have been urgent reasons for dealing with flies and vermin among the forces in Mesopotamia this year, and I was fortunate in being sent up at the end of April to investigate and decide what could be done. Even on the way up, there was entomological work to do. The hospital ship on which I travelled from Bombay had been long in the tropics and was full of small red ants which were a sore trouble to the wounded and sometimes worse. As the ship was going up empty, there was full scope for work and after failing with one method, we succeeded with another. Baits were put down (usually syrup on rags) and the trail of ants to the nest traced back. The nests are all behind wood-casings and the cracks of exits were oiled with a mixture of paraffin and lubricating oil. This isolates the nest inside with the queens and the workers outside cannot bring food in. In three days there were no more trails or nests discoverable and the plague was under control.

To fully appreciate it the abundance of flies has to be seen and still more to be suffered. The tents and trenches are full of them. By night they sleep in masses on tent roofs etc., in the morning they awake to furious activity as soon as the sun has warmed them, till midday they feed and fly and buzz; then they seek deep cool shelter if it is hot, say over 110°F. in the tent, and go to sleep. In my tent they preferred to get under the bed on the sides of the pit in which one lives. At evening they start again and are very active from 5 to 7. When one has been driven crazy, it is good to go and see the patient resignation of the sick and wounded and therefrom to learn control and resolve more strenuously to destroy the scourge. And then one remembers that nearly every disease in Mesopotamia is one that is carried by water and flies only, and one realizes that the fly is really a serious factor in this campaign.

Another entomological problem is of some importance in Mesopotamia, and this is the control of vermin and sand-flies, fortunately no difficult matter. The former convey relapsing fever and typhus, the latter carry sand-fly fever; both are the cause of irritation, the sand-fly especially; there have been cases of serious septic sores from sand-fly bites and the sand-fly has been one of the real plagues of life. Fortunately there is a cure for both. In 1904, the use of Crude Oil Emulsion was first introduced by the Entomological Section for vermin on animals; early in 1915, a refined form was shown to the War Office, and in May was adopted as the official vermin remedy for the army. It is now being made in large quantities in Bombay and sent up to Mesopotamia. In the Army it is known as 'Vermijelli', but as this is a registered name, the property of a firm in London, it is called 'Sand-fly and Vermin Ointment'. It has the merit of keeping off sand-flies and mosquitoes, if rubbed very lightly on the hands and face. I had one tube with me in Mesopotamia. I did not realize the sand-fly was there and was badly bitten the first night; I was never bitten again, I used no net and all who shared my tube found the same. It is now being issued for this purpose. For vermin the emulsion is rubbed on the hairy parts of the body and on the seams of clothing; under-clothes are washed with it and dried without rinsing so that the clothes are lightly impregnated with it.

The breeding places in camps, trenches, etc., are of three kinds. The latrine trench is far the worst, accounting for probably 90 per cent. of the flies; the accumulations of stable manure, and the accumulation of refuse and offal account for the rest. The latrine trenches are about 18 inches deep, a foot long, six inches across; a series are dug side by side, according to the number of men. They are filled up daily. They offer the ideal breeding place for flies and they swarm with flies laying eggs when they are in use and are solid masses of maggots in a few days. Flies emerge from trenching grounds in hordes, get their first meal at the nearest trench then in use and then distribute themselves over the camp. Stable manure was comparatively harmless owing to rapid desiccation; only when small amounts were swept up with dry litter and so preserved from drying did one find maggots and the manure is nearly all dried and burnt. Kitchen refuse and offal are usually burnt or buried but would easily breed flies. The greatest care is usually taken and it is only carelessness on the part of the sweepers or camp cleaners that allows this material to breed flies.

In most places in Mesopotamia there is absolutely no other source of fly breeding; the land is flat, dry, absolutely barren as a rule; there is no shade, a fierce sun bakes it, a dry wind blows furiously. Only where man is, can there be shelter, food or breeding places and there is no man but soldiers in the war area. There are stories of bodies of men trekking into the bare open country and finding hordes of flies, but they took these with them. When one comes out of the trenches, flies settle on all the areas shaded by one's *topee* or oneself and on all the shady parts of one's horse; they travel on one thus for miles, unable to fly away in the fierce sun. In this way one carries swarms of flies and a body of men, when they camp, will naturally find their tents full of flies.

Then one sees the operating tent and realizes that flies may come 100 yards from a nearby latrine to vomit their last food on the exposed tissues of a patient; one sees flies settling on a fresh wound; and the men fighting them off while it is dressed.

A short simple set of instructions was prepared and issued; the measures recommended are discussed here in turn.

1. As far as possible, replace latrine trenches by tins and incinerate…
2. Where incineration is impossible and deep trenching is impossible, then each latrine must be treated…a trench treated with oil does not get infected with maggots and if oiled when it is filled up, many maggots are killed…
3. Oil should be used even with tins as it prevents flies settling and feeding on the excreta…
4. Kitchen refuse and offal are to be burned or oiled and buried. This is obvious and is rendered more important by the fact that a great many goats are slaughtered by native regiments, in their own way, near their lines. There is a great deal of indiscriminate goat-killing going on wherever there are native units and this material would breed flies. The absence of blue-bottles shows how careful the men are in this matter.
5. Horse and mule droppings are to be collected and burned or spread out to dry…
6. Trial of fly poisoning with sodium arsenite showed it to be an extremely effective method; fortunately I had been able in Bombay to get 50 tons of weed killer, which was crude arsenite and worked very well.

   A mixture is made of arsenite half a pound, *gur* [sticky brown sugar or molasses] two and a half pounds, water two and a half gallons. This is a convenient amount for a kerosene tin. In this a gunny bag [a jute sack] was dipped and hung up. A shelter tent or a covering of mats is advisable or the flies will not come in the hottest part of the day, and the gunny bag must be kept moist. Flies come in swarms, feed and die on the spot. The solution is weak enough not to affect them till they have fed; if made too strong, they are affected before they get a fatal dose. It is possible to fit up strips of gunny on the roller towel principle so that it dips in the tin; as it dries and gets too concentrated water is added … The slaughter is very great and the effective range appears to be at least 200 yards and is probably much more. This means that to keep a camp clear one wants a fly-poisoning station every quarter of a mile or so …

7. In the trenches flies collect in masses at certain places at night and at midday. They particularly like canvas or tarpaulin coverings and sheltered corners in dug-outs. With a spraying machine and suitable liquid, one can kill flies in bulk …

8. Hospital tents and buildings require other methods. Formaline can be used for fly poisoning; but the 'Miscible fly spray' used in Europe and Egypt will probably give the best results; it is undesirable to use the oil as it taints milk and food; but this new fly spray, whose laboratory name is *Exol*, is being sent up for hospital use. It is not poisonous or inflammable and has only a slight smell; it does not taint food. It is mixed with water and sprayed in the air. Flies fall to the ground paralysed or dead …

A special problem arises in the case of bodies of men moving. I believe that it is better in these cases to have no trench latrines, but to mark off a space of clean and hard ground and use that. The heat and dryness is such that flies cannot breed in the material which desiccates at once. This goes against the sanitary expert's ideas but I believe it to be sound in all cases where the moving body is not going to stay more than three days.

… I returned to India to organize supplies of arsenic, sprayers, etc., and to get eight men … They were recruited from the entomological and mycological sections [at Pusa] with one from the veterinary staff. They have rank as Indian Warrant Officers according to their pay and will be on duty in Mesopotamia probably till October. In the first place they join Captain Beeson to get experience of military conditions and then they will be posted out.

That this was not quite the whole story, we learn from his son.

His brother-in-law, the Army one I mentioned, my mother's brother, was also in the Mespot campaign. And he was a prisoner of the Turks at Kut. So he told me all about it. I heard a lot about that campaign. My father's part in it was very short. He got beri-beri quite quickly and was invalided back to India and then sent back to England. The troops were going down with dysentery and things like that and he was called in and given the rank of Lieutenant Colonel. He was a very unmilitary man. Anyway he got this honorary rank but he didn't last very long. Beri-beri is a deficiency disease. He seemed to recover from it. There were no after effects. Perhaps they were a bit quick in pulling him out, I don't know.

Before returning to England, he found the time to complete his *Report* on the silk industry with Mr Ansorge, most probably from a base at Pusa.

CHAPTER **XVI**

As the Professor's leave from Imperial College was to ·expire in December 1916, we must suppose that he had returned to England by that time to take up his routine duties.

Where we were between '15 and '19 I can't remember. My parents were away so much that we didn't really have a permanent home. All their houses were taken on long rents. Such a good idea. A lot of our present misfortunes are due to everybody insisting on buying a house. I was still at Prep School in Seaford. I spent my holidays with aunts and saw little of either parent at this important stage of my life, except one short holiday at Caister, in Norfolk. I remember once, in 1917, I was staying with one of the aunts in a place called East Dereham and there was an airfield very close, it was just a field. And one night a message came to us – I don't know if it was on the 'phone or not – that a zeppelin raid was expected. We all got out of bed, took some blankets and someone put a mattress on top of the dining room table and we all huddled underneath, expecting to hear bombs. But as far as I remember we didn't hear any; though there were some. The next morning we hitched the pony to the trap and drove over to this airfield and we saw some chap there and he said O yes there was an air raid – there are some bomb craters over there. But they were such shallow things I thought it's not been much of an air raid – fuss for nothing. On another occasion I was staying with another aunt in Blackheath and the zeppelin was shot down by a pilot – he just had to fire a tracer bullet into the gas bag and that was that. I've always rather regretted missing that.

In December 1913, at the end of his interview on the tse-tse fly, the Professor mentioned that a visit to Australia was still under discussion. The problem then had been the Blow Fly which attacks sheep, but by 1916 a new pest was causing untold havoc among stored grain which could not be moved owing to the shortage of shipping. The U-boat campaign had been particularly successful in 1915 and 1916.

There is a long section on Weevils, the *Curculionidae*, in *Indian Insect Life*.

> Though the family is a very large one, the life-histories of only a very few are known. So far as known, the eggs are of two types; eggs laid in exposed positions on the outside of a plant are small oval objects, smooth, with a hard shell; those which are deposited in the tissues are soft, elongate and white. They are laid singly, and usually in considerable number spread over a number of plants. Larvae are, as a rule, internal feeders and white, soft, legless grubs... None are known to be other than herbivorous... The weevils which emerge are active insects, diurnal or nocturnal, feeding on leaves and other parts of plants or on plant sap.

The Rice and Wheat Weevils are specifically mentioned as attacking stored grains. The Wheat Weevils are thus described:

> Calandra (Sitophilus) is a genus of two species of world-wide occurrence. *C. granaria*, L., is of a uniform deep redbrown colour, the prothorax with oblong punctures. It is wingless. *C. oryzae*, Linn., has two fulvous patches on each elytron, the punctures on the prothorax are rounded and closer together, the metathoracic episternum is wider and has two rows of punctures. It is winged, the weevils flying readily. The latter is the common Indian species, of which much has been written, but little is known.

This was the situation in 1909. By 1916 further investigation at Pusa, carried out by Messrs Barnes and Groves, had established that the female weevil required a minimum of 8 per cent moisture in order to penetrate the wheat grain and lay her single egg within it. These findings were published in a *Memoir* by the Department of Agriculture in India in November 1916 and they must have been known to the Professor. Possibly a copy of the *Memoir* had arrived in Australia, possibly not. If a copy of *Indian Insect Life* had been sent there, there is no reason to suppose that anyone had actually read it.

Similarly, the method of 'bulk-storing' grain in India, that is to say without putting it into bags, must have been well known to the Professor. For centuries the grain had been stored in pits, or in structures of dried mud, closely covered with packed earth and completely airtight. The Great Granary at Bankipore, a few miles from Pusa, built in 1786, was an enormous upturned bowl of masonry, with an external staircase. The grain was poured into it, loose, at the top, and taken out again from the bottom. It was completely watertight and the hot suns of the pre-monsoon months made sure that the internal temperature was much too high for weevils.

If any of this were known at high scientific levels in Australia, it was quite certainly not known to the wheat-growers of New South Wales and Victoria. Even if it had been, it would have been hotly disputed or just simply ridiculed.

In November 1916 the Government of the United Kingdom agreed to purchase three million tons of wheat from Australia. Russia, hitherto the largest exporter of wheat in Europe, was suffering from war conditions and from diminished harvests; and in 1916 the British Government was informed that the North American wheat crop was likely to be lower than usual. The three million tons were therefore of enormous importance both to a Britain already on bread rationing and to the Australian farmers who faced bankruptcy if they were not sold.

The wheat, in thirteen million jute bags which would have required two hundred ships to transport them, was stacked in hastily erected sheds near the docks, put up by the railway companies and leased to the farmers. A plague of mice immediately followed. In June 1917 the Victoria Vermin Destruction Department reported that it had destroyed thirteen *tons* of mice in three days, at eight railway sidings. Means of protecting the wheat from mice were swiftly devised, but no sooner was this achieved than the stacks were attacked by weevils.

It was received wisdom among the growers at this time that the weevil germ was carried within every grain of wheat and they would not listen to any scientific information on the life history of the weevil. The wheat-growers themselves appear to have been of a peculiarly obdurate kind. As early as 1908 a Royal Commission on wheat marketing, trying to convince the growers in South Australia of the virtues of bulk handling, refers to 'the apathy of the growers' and also to 'the unfriendly attitude of the wheat shippers'. The wheat continued to be stored in jute bags imported from India, bringing with them their own insect predators, in particular the Khapra Beetle. The bags were also very attractive to mice.

In November 1916, the Director of Chemistry for South Australia wrote that they had found it more difficult to deal with the wheat men than with the weevils.

> We might have settled the weevil long ago if we had had a free hand, but the opinions of so many people having preconceived notions upon spontaneous generation had to be overcome and this has hampered our work in every way. The general attitude towards us has been one of amusement at our attempts to tackle a hopeless job. So long as our efforts did not interfere with time-honoured customs we were indulgently allowed to carry on our investigations, but when we wanted new methods of handling and storing wheat we were 'up against compression'. The wheat men are generally great theorists, the scientific men are extremely practical by comparison...We have had stacks of clean wheat set down within a few yards of weevily wheat, and so thousands of pounds of wheat have been sacrificed.

The three officials in Australia to be principally concerned with the problem were Mr Leo Rossell, representing the wheat trade; Professor W.A. Haswell, from the Department of Biology at Sydney University, and Mr W.W. Froggatt, the Government Entomologist for New South Wales. It was on instructions from the latter that the stacks had recently been sprayed with sea water, on the understanding that weevils could not stand salt.

A Grain Insects Committee had been set up in London in 1916, to research the different methods of controlling insects in stored wheat. There was also a Royal Commission on Wheat Supplies based in London. In response to a request from them, the Commonwealth Advisory Council for Science and Industry in Melbourne – then the seat of the Commonwealth Government – agreed to co-operate with the Committees in London, and with the larger dominions of the British Empire, 'to consider the relative economic importance of insects infecting grain, to suggest measures to combat them, and to enquire into the actual loss from these pests or other aspects of this question in Australia.'

In October 1917 the Committee in London wrote to the Advisory Council: 'We think the difficulties in all these experiments are due to the want of someone to deal with the problem continually, from a scientific point of view.'

A brisk exchange of cables followed between London and the Prime Minister's Office in Melbourne. The upshot was a formal request, from the Royal Commission on Wheat Supplies to Imperial College, that Professor Lefroy should be released to deal with these problems, for one year certainly, or until the end of the War, without prejudice to his Professorship.

This is dated the 24th of October 1917. The request was granted and, a week or two later, the Professor sailed to America and crossed the continent to San Francisco.

> Where my mother and I stayed while Father was in Australia I do not recollect, apart from a short period in 'digs' at Richmond.

In San Francisco Harold was joined by Mr R.A. Love, of the Wheat Board, and they sailed for Sydney on the 11th of December, arriving on the 9th of January. Here they were greeted by Mr Rossell, Professor Haswell and Mr Froggatt.

His departure, and their arrival, were both reported in the London *Times*.

He went immediately to examine the conditions of storage at Enfield, and other depots, outside Sydney. He found some two million bushels of wheat stored under corrugated iron roofs which sagged on to the sacks of wheat, letting in the rain. Sacking was drawn across the sides of the sheds, by no means keeping out either the rain or the moisture blown in off the sea. Sacks at the bottom of the stacks were torn and damp, offering plentiful food to the mice and ideal breeding conditions to the weevils.

On the 15th of January, within a week of his arrival in Australia, the Professor sent the following memorandum to London, and to the Advisory Council, from Sydney:

Examination of wheat stacks has shown

1. New 1917–18 crop must be stacked apart from infected old crop. Least safe distance is 100 yards.
2. Constant breeding of weevils at base of stacks, mainly due to burst bags, or punctured bags.
   a. Sleepers must be laid with air space under the stack.
   b. Ground under sleepers must be made unsuitable by a 2-inch layer of napthalin, with lime or other powdered material, like tar oil powdered.
   c. Bags must be intact.
3. Old infested wheat stacks must be cleaned up. A system of clearing weevils out of this wheat is in trial and will shortly be perfected; but if old wheat is moved in it is essential that the site be really cleared of insects. Infection readily occurs from old stacks if these are not cleared up, and the immense accumulation of insects in the spilled wheat is left untreated. When a stack is cleared the ground under should be liberally treated either with the napthalin lime mixture or with some other insecticidal powder, such as tar oil and lime, or tar oil and ground slag. If not these insects will migrate to other stacks.
4. Damage to wheat is put down to weevils, but this term really covers at least six different insects, of which three pass stages of their life inside the grain, and it is essential to realise that there is not only one insect involved, but several, with different habits and life histories.
5. Assuming that all new wheat is stacked remote from the old, on a properly aerated base, with insecticidal powder on the ground, with board and hessian floor, with a roof carried independently and not liable to collapse, there should be no further damage from weevil

and insects if the sides of the stack are protected against rain and moisture, and if the wheat is reasonably dry to start with.

6. The removal of infected wheat to mills or elsewhere must be properly done: as soon as details of the treatment of infected wheat are available they will be circulated; but it is essential that infected wheat stacks be not moved unless proper precautions are taken to deal with the sites and prevent infection of new grain stacks.

7. It is impossible to visit all areas at once; but it is possible to advise as to any action being taken and to assist with the problem, if those handling wheat will refer questions here: samples of infected wheat can also be examined and reported on: and much loss will probably be avoided if advice is taken as to the effect of any action proposed on the weevil and its breeding. It is clear that the proper handling of wheat to avoid insect attack has not been considered adequately; action has been taken which has assisted weevil attack, and it is now possible to refer questions of this kind and obtain advice. So far as possible this must be dealt with by correspondence.

8. A great part of the available wheat is to be shipped and it cannot be shipped if infected with weevil, as the insect develops so strongly during the voyage. A very mild infection of insects which to grain handlers appears immaterial, will make the wheat unsuitable for shipment. Infected wheat may not show an abundance of insects sufficient to be noticed by the ordinary man, but this wheat may still be too infected to ship. For this reason a system of treating grain, that will absolutely destroy all insect life in it, is being worked out, and as soon as possible details will be circulated.

An experiment carried out in Australia had actually proved that forty weevils could, within three months, produce three thousand descendants.

Either the Memorandum itself, or a report on it, must have been made public as, on the 5th of February, the *Sydney Morning Herald* carried a substantial article entitled: 'On the Land. Protect the Wheat.'

We have lost enough as it is through bad management and incapacity in handling our wheat crop, and to that amount there is no necessity to add more. Professor Lefroy has shown us how we can handle this wheat, and keep it fit for export. It is a matter of the State Wheat Board following the example of the British Commission; of utilising local engineering facilities, and having machines made that will both dry the wheat and clean out any weevil that is present. There is no patent royalty to pay, or any charge for the advice; we have but to follow a straight course ahead. Yet so far there is no evidence that the Wheat Board is doing anything in the matter…

Seeing what we have lost through weevil it is an extraordinary position that a stranger should come here, and in five weeks have these machines proved and near completion, while the State Wheat Board, with all the facilities it should be able to command, has done nothing in regard to the weevil trouble. But we can only be grateful that the way out has now been made plain, and what is required now is that the State should follow Professor Lefroy's advice, and order sufficient of these machines to dry all the wet wheat, and ensure that nothing but perfectly dry wheat goes into the stacks at the permanent depots. It is a case of the first cost being the cheapest cost.

The machines referred to were later described by the Professor in a lecture given on the 8th of April and recorded in the *Journal of the Royal Society of New South Wales*.

The electrical method of endeavouring to destroy them by high voltages was ineffectual, as with a charge of 63,000 volts between two metallic plates, the insects simply stood on end, and when the current was disconnected, they ran off the plate. One cannot get the current to go through the weevils.

The method of destroying them by heat remained. In this connection, it has been found that if the grain is subjected to a temperature of 140°F. for three minutes, all the weevil is killed. The desideratum is to get a machine which will effectually and expeditiously heat the body of the grain to this temperature, so that the pest will be killed and the grain will not be cooked. Most of the machines designed for this purpose depend upon the grain being heated by hot air, and because of the greater specific heat of the grain as compared with the air, it has been determined that 1,000 gallons of air are necessary to heat up one gallon of grain. The machine must, therefore, have a large air capacity. Many types of machines have been made by various makers within the last few months, and the principles underlying their mechanics were illustrated by the lecturer with the aid of a lantern. Some, as the Robinson machine, are already treating wheat, others are in the experimental stage.

From the same report we learn that:

> Grain with 8% of moisture is proof against weevil, and even with 10% it is fairly safe. Wheat will never absorb more than under 2% of moisture from damp air, even under extreme conditions, so that if it is stacked with 8% of moisture it should be fairly safe from weevil…damp grain serves as a breeding centre for the weevil.
>
> Various disinfectants have been tried, but…A good disinfectant has not yet been obtained.

The *Sydney Morning Herald* continued to report the Professor's activities with articles on the 8th, 9th, 12th, 15th and 16th of February. On the 14th, however, it was obliged to report that the Professor was ill in hospital, though the nature of his illness was not disclosed.

It cannot be supposed that the swiftness of the Professor's advice, or the efficacy of his remedies, gave very much pleasure to Mr Froggatt or, indeed, to any of the local authorities. Such remedies as they had tried had not been very successful. In January 1918, Mr Frogatt had written to the Advisory Council:

> As you are probably aware the British Wheat Commission are in Sydney, Mr. Love and Professor Lefroy, Imperial Entomologist. I am going round with Lefroy on the weevil question while he is in this State. Later on he is going to Melbourne. If the Council think it advisable I should like to come over with him, work in conjunction with him would be of advantage to our Wheat Diseases Committee.

To which the Council sharply replied:

> Your letter of 2 January has been considered by the Executive. I am directed to inform you that the Executive Committee could hardly agree to the course you propose without knowing Prof. Lefroy's desires on the subject. It seems to them not improbable that the Victorian Government might desire that the State Entomologist should accompany Prof. Lefroy when he is in Victoria and they might perhaps object to your presence in addition.

Mr Froggatt was a particularly energetic man, almost sixty years old, and largely self-educated through observation and fieldwork. He was the author of *Australian Insects* (1907) and of 131 articles on various subjects published in the Australian *Agricultural Gazette* between 1899 and 1906. In 1907 the Australian Government had despatched him to the United States, Europe, India and Ceylon to investigate the habits of the Fruit Fly, a tour which lasted almost two years. He was at this time Lecturer in Entomology in the Department of Agriculture at Sydney University. When it was first proposed that one man should devote his whole time to solving the problem of the damaged wheat, he had recommended a graduate of Sydney University who, he claimed, had all the requisite knowledge both of entomology and chemistry, backed by a wide experience in the field.

To the above reproof he shortly replied:

…I might state that my letter was written before I had seen Mr. Lefroy – I have had several consultations with him since and we agree I think in most things on the wheat problem in Australia. My letter was not written as Entomologist of NSW but as the Entomologist, Federal Wheat Diseases Committee…I do not in any way wish to encroach in the domain of Mr. C. French with whom I have worked in harmony for many years…It might be understood also that I have no desire to interfere with Prof. Lefroy's personal investigations.

This letter is dated the 11th of January, two days after the Professor's arrival in Sydney. Unquestionably, Mr Froggatt's pride had been hurt; he did not accompany the Professor into the State of Victoria.

In view of the uncordial relations that were to exist between them, it is not unreasonable to suppose that the Professor's patrician manner and utterance grated on Mr Froggatt quite as much as his rustic common-sense and confidence grated on the Professor.

CHAPTER XVII

It is not known for how long the Professor remained in hospital, but it seems probable that he began to reflect that, as he had by now solved in the course of a few weeks the problems that he had been engaged to solve in the course of a year, the time had come to return to England. Possibly he said so, because an agitation began, very shortly, to retain his services for consultation on other subjects.

These were: the Sheep Maggot Fly, or Blow Fly, *Lucilia sericata*, which laid its eggs in the wet, or soiled, wool of the sheep. Its larvae would bore into the flesh, ruining the fleece and causing death when present in sufficient numbers; the Prickly Pear, *Opuntia vulgaris*, an edible cactus imported from the Mediterranean, which was rapidly over-running large areas of pasture land; and the St John's Wort, *Hypericum perforatum*, a plant native to Northern Europe, most probably imported with some seed corn and now beginning to menace both wheatfields and pasture.

The matter seems to have been dealt with as one of great importance. A confidential 'Urgent Memo' from the Executive Committee of the Advisory Council to the Prime Minister's Department in Melbourne is dated the 4th of May 1918.

Professor Lefroy's terms

He will not remain in Australia, but might return October next.

He would prefer to work under Commonwealth Government in connection with the Advisory Council…rather than with the Pastoralists Associations.

If offer made to return in October at £3000 for one year, plus travelling expenses, he may accept it.

He would work at big problems only – blow-fly pest, prickly pear, St. John's Wort and other weeds, wheat weevil and the exclusion of other wheat pests, the silk industry etc.

It will be an advantage to do preliminary work in England on prickly pear and St. John's Wort, say in July and August, and that he should be paid half the proposed salary while engaged on the work in England and during voyage.

He will require £2000 for experimental work including temporary staff.

He will require complete liberty of action.

Further on, the same Memo informs us that the Professor's terms have been met and that he has been requested also to investigate a fruit pest, the Woolly Aphis, and has been specifically asked to assist the establishment of a silk industry in Australia.

The writer of the Memo adds:

Professor Lefroy is due to leave Australia on 15th [May]. I go to Sydney on 7th and as I will probably see Lefroy would be glad to receive any instructions from the Acting Prime Minister. Professor Lefroy was not prepared to give an answer until after his return to England, and in any case could not accept without leave from College.

On the 9th of May the Prime Minister's Department informed the Advisory Council that the Commonwealth Government would defray the entire cost of the Professor's engagement and that he would work only in connection with the Council.

On the 14th of May Imperial College telegraphed the Acting Prime Minister, giving immediate leave of absence to the Professor, on the condition that he returned to England by the beginning of October 1919.

With matters at this point, the Professor did in fact sail from Sydney on the 15th of May, for what we must hope was a peaceful and comfortable voyage.

His campaign against the Wheat Weevil had been successful and it was estimated later that if nothing had been done to check the weevils a loss totalling over £11,000,000 would have been sustained in one year alone, 1918–19. The cost of the treatment amounted to a quarter of a million and claims for deterioration, etc. came to slightly more than half a million.

On the 17th of May, the *Sydney Stock and Station Journal* published an article entitled: 'Is He The Best Man? Professor Lefroy and Our Pests. Proposed Federal Appointment.'

> There is an idea current that Professor Maxwell Lefroy is the man to solve our pest problems. In one breath prickly pear, blowfly and weevil are mentioned, and then in the next breath some more are given. Who is this Professor Lefroy; and what has he done? The Stock Journal does not ask the question out of any ill-feeling towards the Professor. We ask the question in the interests of the primary producing industries. If he is the likeliest man, by all means let us have him for the job. But is he? Who says he is, and on what grounds?

A *resumé* of his recent agreement with the Federal Government then follows, as issued from Melbourne, but no figures are quoted. The article then continues:

> So that looks as if he is coming! We hear that Professor Lefroy asks a salary of £3,000 per annum. It is said that the Bureau of Science and Industry considered at first that £1,250 p.a. with £500 expenses was a fair thing. Apparently the Professor has a much higher idea of the value of his services. It is reported that some Victorian pastoralists suggested that he be paid £4,000 a year. The Victorians must be doing well, or believe that the Professor can do well for them! If he can solve one of our biggest pest problems, such as the blowfly or the prickly pear, he would be cheap at £40,000! If Professor Lefroy is paid £3,000 a year, it is six or seven times greater than the salary of the highest paid Government Entomologist in any of our States. Is he worth it? Do his credentials warrant it? Does he stand so far above our own scientists?

As all the figures quoted were absolutely accurate, it was clear that the writer of the article had had intimate knowledge of the negotiations, all of which had been conducted in confidence.

A potted biography of the Professor then follows, without any reference at all to the volume of his published works.

> …he has left no record as a foremost man in the ranks of economic entomologists. His chief work appears to have been as Entomological Lecturer at the Imperial College of Science and Technology at South Kensington, for the last ten years (a kind of Technical College). There is some war work in Mesopotamia to his credit, but its value has not been, as far as we are aware, scientifically assessed.

The rest of this extremely long article is devoted to the thesis that Australian problems can only be solved by Australian scientists as Australia is 'a very peculiar country'.

In its next issue, on the 21st of May, the *Stock Journal* continued:

> As far as the *Stock Journal* knows, the pastoralists associations of Australia are not standing for Professor Lefroy.

> Professor Lefroy has done nothing in Australia to justify the appointment. He certainly did tell us he could make our wheat weevil-proof, and staked his reputation on it. But with all due respect to the Professor, we have only his word for it. Heaven knows, we all hope he can do it, but our point is that his statement that he can does not warrant the Federal Government giving him £3,000 a year and placing him above all the Australian scientists. What has Professor Lefroy done elsewhere that gives the Federal Government sufficient reason to believe that he is head and shoulders above our own men, and is the most likely man to solve our pastoral and agricultural pests' problem? That is what we want to get at.

> We are told that Professor Lefroy will investigate among others, 'diseases affecting the silk industry.' This, incidentally, suggests to us that those responsible for the invitation have a poor idea of relative values, and of what Australia really needs. Australia is not, and does not want to be, much interested in the silk industry. At best, out here, it is only a bit of embroidery that might interest a few women and children. Yet the Professor, who is going to solve the weevil problem for us and look into the blowfly trouble, is supposed to worry about silk diseases! If the

Federal Government made such a suggestion, it is talking trivialities: if the Professor made the proposal, it only goes to bear out our contention that his ignorance of Australian conditions is a fatal handicap.

The second article does not end there. It continues for some time in similar strain. Neither it, nor the first one, was signed, but it is difficult to believe that the author was not Mr W.W. Froggatt, or that the articles were not written with his very close co-operation.

Throughout the Australian winter a correspondence was carried on, largely between the wheat-men and the Advisory Council. It reached the very highest levels.

On the 23rd of May the Acting Prime Minister in Melbourne wrote, to the Prime Minister:

> As you are probably aware, the wool production of Australia has in recent years been very seriously reduced owing to the ravages of blow flies... The Commonwealth Government is anxious to obtain the services of an expert entomologist who has special experience in dealing with flies, and since Professor Lefroy's knowledge is probably unrivalled, an offer was made to him during his recent visit to Australia in the hope of inducing him to remain a further year.

The genus *Lucilia* is mentioned only very briefly in *Indian Insect Life*, in the section, certainly, written by Mr F.M. Howlett; but it *is* mentioned. Neither it, nor the sheep on which it preyed, was unique, or even indigenous, to Australia.

The emphasis of the correspondence began to shift, from the Wheat Weevil to the Blow Fly. On the 28th of May a letter from the President of the New South Wales Pastoral Committee – for investigation of the Blow Fly pest – states that he has noted with satisfaction that the Federal Government has arranged for Professor Lefroy to undertake the work.

In July, the Australian Natives Association of New South Wales passed a resolution of protest against the appointment of Professor Lefroy and this was forwarded to the Advisory Council 'for favour of a reply'. Only its receipt was acknowledged.

On the 17th of August, the Professor cabled the Prime Minister that he would arrive in Melbourne in October. On the 23rd, *The Times* reported:

Professor Maxwell Lefroy, Professor of Entomology at the Imperial College of Science, South Kensington, has accepted a year's engagement with the Commonwealth Government for £3,000, plus £2,000 for experiments. He will investigate the blowfly, the grain weevil, the woolly aphis, prickly pear, and the St. John's Wort. It is estimated that the blowfly caused the loss of sheep in one season to the value of £300,000.

A meeting of the Advisory Council on the 28th of August records that the Professor will be attached only to the Advisory Council and will have a free hand in conducting all his investigations. His conditions had apparently all been met.

On the 2nd of September, however, he wrote to the Acting Prime Minister:

I have been in communication with the High Commissioner and the Rt. Hon. Mr. Hughes, my desire to have you cancel the appointment as Commonwealth Entomologist.

My reason is solely this, that a Sydney paper contained on 17 and 21 May articles relating to my appointment and to me personally which were based on confidential discussions and letters available only to members of the Executive Committee and to members of the Pastoral Blowfly Committee; it is evident that a member of the latter inspired the articles and gave the information; it is quite clear who that member is; and as I have received nothing from the Committee I assume they approve and in fact authorised them.

Under these circumstances it is impossible for me to work with this Committee and I have asked to have the appointment cancelled. In this I am supported by colleagues at the College and the Imperial Entomological Bureau, and I am taking steps to see how far a legal action will be in order to clear up this matter with the Australian pastoralists and public.

At the High Commissioner's office I am urged that the Commonwealth Government can see that the facilities I require can be given in this case, where an official of a State Government is supported by his Premier and Government. I cannot see that the Commonwealth Government can secure the facilities in that State and as I should want to work through the Sydney Pastoral Committee the only possible solution is the removal of the author of the article. Otherwise I should feel that in all my work with the Committee, fresh confidential matter was being collected to form a fresh attack on my work and on myself. I have never worked under such conditions and I do not intend to.

I regret that I did not see this article before I cabled to say I would arrive; but as it is clearly useless to compel an unwilling man, I assume you will accede to my suggestion that my appointment be cancelled.

It would be interesting to know who actually drew the Professor's attention to the two articles, as the *Sydney Stock and Station Journal* was not precisely a publication with an international circulation.

On the 20th of September the Professor wrote again to the Acting Prime Minister:

> In my previous letter I told you of my action in regard to the High Commissioner, I have repeatedly phoned and written to him but can get only the information that the matter is in Mr. Hughes' hands. As I can get nothing else I assume the matter has not been referred to you and that you still anticipate my arrival. If this is so I am sorry, but it is not my fault. It is now a month since I wrote to Mr. Fisher and I can wait no longer. I am therefore proceeding with my college work and taking no further steps about my journey. I am sorry that I can obtain no answer from Mr. Hughes, not even the return of the memento I left at Australia House. I think you will not expect me to be willing to take up work in Australia under the Commonwealth on these conditions.

This letter was written from Westbrook House, Heston, now a part of London Airport.

> It was a large house with an enormous garden. Orchard. Outhouses. Father conveyed that he expected me to earn my pocket money working in the garden. But I much preferred cricket on the lawn. Weeding. A fairly menial task. I didn't like the gardener at all. He came with the house. We had a big staff. Butler, parlour maid, cook. And amongst the furnishings there was a reversible dining-table – the underside was a three-quarter size billiard table. Father would encourage me to play and got quite keen on playing himself. This is when I first felt close to him and he at ease with

me; for once we shared a common interest, to which a second was added
about now, when I became keen on collecting butterflies and moths and
he would take me to the Natural History Museum. Sometimes we went
to the village pond together to collect water insects. He played the 'cello
but did not give any soirees at home. He went to nearby houses or just
strummed by himself to an audience of two. I showed no interest in music
and he did not try to encourage me to learn a musical instrument.

The family was to live at Westbrook House until 1923, their first
experience of settled life since leaving Pusa. On the 25th of September,
the Professor wrote to Imperial College to say that he would return
to them for the current university year and, in all probability, closed
his mind to any prospect of going back to Australia. He formally
declined the Commonwealth Government's offer to him on the 20th
of November 1918, nine days after the end of the Great War.

But the matter did not end there, in Australia. It grumbled on, in
fact, for several years. In September Mr Froggatt complained to the
Advisory Council that he had been given no funds to carry out further
investigation. It is possible that the Advisory Council did not consider
further investigation necessary. In October the Council issued the
Professor's recommendations in the form of a Bulletin, mentioning
that only carbon dioxide was effective as a fumigant – the cost of
which was prohibitive – and stating that wheat stored dry was safe
from attack by weevils.

Mr Rossell and Mr Froggatt continued to observe experiments
using lime; and a Progress Report of the 10th of October mentions
that experiments with moisture were still being conducted.

On the 15th of October Mr James Kidd, President of the Pastoral
Committee, had written to the Professor: 'Until yesterday when the
matter was brought to my attention by a representative of one of the
newspapers, I had not seen nor was I aware of the existence of the
articles in the Stock and Station Journal.'

He disclaimed all knowledge of the articles, referred to
'irresponsible journalists' and concluded: 'You were assured of every

possible assistance from this Committee in your investigations and this attitude has never altered.'

In October the Australian Wheat Board had cabled the Professor to ask if carbon dioxide would damage the food value of wheat. He had replied that it would not. The Wheat Board also sent instructions, based on the Professor's recommendations, to the Agriculture Bureau, for information of the farmers.

Then on the 16th of December, four additions were made to a pamphlet designed for distribution to the farmers. They were suggested by Mr Leo Rossell and they were:

(a) The idea of spontaneous generation of weevils was to be specifically contradicted.
(b) If a farmer finds weevils in his wheat, then it is evident that his preventive measures are ineffective. He should take measures to seal his barns and use carbon bisulphide to destroy the weevils.
(c) A warning should be given against mixing new with old wheat.
(d) Pictures of the insects should be included.

In view of this, it can be concluded that the Professor's visit to Australia was not entirely in vain; but it proved impossible to lure him back. He never returned, neither was he ever consulted about any other Australian problem. It was a complete victory for the wheat-men.

Bulk storage, the only permanent remedy against the Wheat Weevil, did not become general in Australia until 1954. The Prickly Pear finally succumbed to a vegetarian ladybird in the 1960s; *Indian Insect Life* mentions that the genus *Epilachna* 'is herbivorous and universally distributed'. The St John's Wort and the Woolly Aphis were controlled by herbicides and pesticides developed after the Second World War.

There is no silk industry in Australia, and the Sheep Blow Fly was conquered by the simple expedient of stripping the hairy skin off the backsides of young lambs, removing the soiled wool in which the Blow Fly laid its eggs.

CHAPTER **XVIII**

.

With the gradual return of 'peace-time conditions', the
Professor was able to devote some time to his one remaining
commitment outside Imperial College, the Insect House at the Zoo.
In her autobiography, *Things Worth While* (Hutchinson, 1957), Evelyn
Cheesman, later to become, among other things, head of that same
Insect House, wrote:

> When war work ended (Neutral and Enemy Trade Index) with the
> declaration of peace I took the opportunity of my first leisure to repair a
> deficiency, namely to improve my performance on the typewriter, which
> was rudimentary. Nobody among my acquaintances in Croydon could
> offer me the hire of a typewriter by the hour. But, while enquiring, a
> friend told me that Grace Lefroy in the Imperial Institute was offering to
> anybody willing to improve their typing the use of an office typewriter
> in return for secretarial work...
>
> Out of the blue came a letter from Grace Lefroy: 'How would you
> like a post at the Zoo? My cousin Maxwell is looking everywhere for
> somebody to take charge of the Insect House at the Zoo, of which he
> is curator. It is work that a woman can do and no special knowledge
> is needed.'
>
> Grace and I had often discussed wild flowers, animal pets and
> nature generally, and she knew of my plans to become a vet. She knew
> that my lunch hours were spent in the Natural History Museum. Now,
> with her zeal in fitting round pegs into round holes, she urged me to

accept, and made an appointment for me to meet Professor Lefroy at the Zoo.

When first introduced to the Insect House I was rather appalled, and very uncertain whether I could shoulder such a responsibility. Professor Lefroy was very despondent, as he had received many refusals. It was the end of the War certainly, but the keeper had not been released from the Army; the work of cleaning the place was being shared by keepers of the adjoining Small Mammal Houses. The House was very much neglected, there were so few exhibits that it was ignored by visitors as unworthy of a visit. My heart sank into my boots. Most of the glass-fronted cages were empty; one lonely aquatic beetle swam in the largest tank...On my last visit to the Zoo some years previously, there had been a fascinating display of exotic forms, moths, beetles, scorpions, centipedes...

We adjourned to the Professor's 'office', which was part of a storeroom in the basement of the Society's offices. He had there a large table for unpacking and arranging exhibitions, a register for accessions, a folio in which records of the most successful exhibits were kept, with food, dates of stages in the life-history, and so forth. The department was not very well equipped, but I should be given a free hand in developing it along any lines I thought likely to be successful. A few days' grace was allowed me to make up my mind whether to take it on...I agreed to take it on for a fortnight on trial and then decide.

She did take it on. On the 28th of April 1919, *The Times* announced:

Assistant Curator Miss Cheesman is to be available every Saturday 2–5 pm, to give advice on insects to allotment holders and small cultivators. People will be asked to leave specimens of insects and within a few days Miss Cheesman will report on whether harmful and the most economical method of eradicating. There will be no charge.

Miss Cheesman continues:

There was a most welcome opportunity for attending a course on entomology under Professor Lefroy at the Royal College of Science (as it was then named). For two years I managed two mornings or afternoons weekly attending his lectures while he was in England, or studying myself with the rest of his students. Lefroy was an erratic teacher, but his lectures had the merit of being unusually interesting. Every one of his students acknowledged that, although we all felt discouraged by the lack of a satisfactory grounding – Taxonomy, for example – the science of classification – was not taught and this is of primary importance. There were few textbooks published, no examinations were held and no diplomas presented. I owe a great deal to my fellow students for we exchanged views and information in close cooperation. My notes made at that period were the scaffolding on which later knowledge was erected, a bit shaky in places but the essentials were there.

The Professor was once more lecturing to learned societies outside the College. He gave a course of four at the Royal Institution in Albemarle Street at the beginning of the year. On the 28th of February 'Silk from Wild Insects'; on the 5th of March 'Insect Enemies of our Food Supply'; and on the 12th and 19th of March 'Insect problems: bollworm, death watch beetles, etc.'

In April he was once more re-considering the course offered to his students, returning to his pre-war contention that there was far too much emphasis on zoology, and that nothing like enough attention was being paid to plants and their diseases. He considered that students should be fully trained in the chemistry of insecticides, the life histories of disease-carrying insects, all methods of spraying and all relevant machinery, and that they should also have a knowledge of all existent legislation. His new proposals were as follows:

1. Ground-work for the first year
2. General biology including geology and organic chemistry
3. Enough botany to enable a student to take later courses in plant physiology, pathology and fungi. This is absolutely essential
4. Applied entomology
5. Technical training to fit a student for research or government entomology – rearing, identifying, illustrating, writing reports, general investigation
6. Medical entomology. Insects as disease carriers. Household pests, grain insects
7. Research. Every student in his fourth year should work out, or make a start on a problem

Every irrelevant item of instruction was to be eliminated. Applied entomology had become too specialised and technical. The facts, the data, the experience with insecticides, the legislation – they were all there. Zoology must be separated from entomology as too much time was spent on the detailed study of animals and not enough on the practical, everyday work of checking insect pests.

During the year, with the consent of Professor McBride of Zoology, the course in entomology was altered as the Professor wished. His students confined their zoological studies to animals of economic importance.

The seventh of the above proposals is particularly interesting. The Professor himself possessed a highly original, enquiring mind, at its best following its own lines of thought. He had demanded 'a free hand' from the Australian Government; he had offered Miss Cheesman 'a free hand'. The fact that, as Miss Cheesman records, there was no instruction in taxonomy may well be because, quite probably, the Professor had mastered the principles of taxonomy before he left Marlborough. He might have expected all other students of entomology to have done so at a similar stage in their lives.

He is on record as having said that researching entomologists should not *also* have to be administrators. There is no doubt that his administrative work was a burden to him. At its lowest level, the situation in Australia can be considered as a simple conflict between an original thinker, able to take more than one step at a time, and an entrenched administration, able to proceed only with caution and along lines previously laid down and tested.

The Australian affair still lumbered on. On the 10th of April, the College Secretary wrote to the Professor, informing him that the Australian Prime Minister, Mr Hughes, had asked for his services for a year, but that the College had turned down the request 'with great regret'.

On the 14th, the Professor replied, accepting their decision, but regretting that he was being given no opportunity to give his views on the progress of entomology, as he had personally done so much to forward its importance, in America, Australia and India. To which the Rector, Sir Alfred Keogh, replied, on the 30th of April, that he was glad to see the Professor at any time, but that if he would attend more meetings of the College Board of Studies, he would have an excellent chance to put his case.

In May, a sombre note is struck. A doctor's certificate states that the Professor is suffering from neurasthenia and weak action of the heart, due to mental overstrain. 'He should take things as easily as possible for a time, and avoid anything in the way of excessive mental work and worry.' The report for April in the next year is substantially the same.

Neurasthenia is defined, in a dictionary of the time, as: an atonic condition of the nervous system; functional nervous weakness; nervous debility. The word 'atonic' is defined as 'wanting tone or nervous elasticity'. For the patient, it would have meant an almost complete loss of physical energy, combined with a considerable reduction in enthusiasm, deeply distressing to one of his habitual optimism. He was also liable to become seriously depressed.

In June he wrote to Sir Alfred Keogh to say that he proposed to resign as soon as he could find another post. He had felt unsettled at the College since the death of Adam Sedgwick and no demonstrator had arrived to replace him. His relations with the Professor of Zoology were unpleasant. While the Zoology Department had only five students, Entomology had seventeen, but more money was being spent on the zoologists. His students had diverse needs which the College did not supply – he supplied them himself with money earned by outside work. 'The main collections we use are mine; the library is mine. I pay wholly for the work done here and for the Saturday spraying excursions which are absolutely necessary as part of a student's practical training.'

Furthermore, the College was proposing an increase in his teaching hours, ignoring the hours spent outside the College. A list of his hours is enclosed, together with a request for a contribution towards the cost of running Westbrook House.

It is a letter from a demoralised, discouraged man. His son recalls:

> My father's Australian experience would certainly have bruised his sensitive nature, long accustomed to dealing with no less sensitive and well-bred Indians. His practice when encountering hostile or discordant circumstances was purely defensive, like that of the hedgehog. No ranting or raving. For that reason perhaps I never once heard him refer to Australia.

No answer to his letter exists in the Imperial College files. Perhaps it was ignored, as being from a sick man. Perhaps his grievances were put right. Only one thing is absolutely certain; his resignation was not accepted.

On the 12th of June, the Science Standing Committee of the RIBA paid a second visit to Westminster Hall to inspect the repairs that were still in progress, to strengthen and maintain the roof. Their Report, issued later in the year, informs us that:

> The characteristic orange-brown colour of the old timber was carefully preserved by the exclusion of any substance that had the effect of changing or darkening its hue. After considerable experiment, both in the laboratory and in Westminster Hall, a prescription by Dr. Maxwell Lefroy, of the Imperial College of Science, South Kensington, was adopted. In preparation for spraying, the timber is first carefully cleaned and freed from dust by means of an air blast and then all surfaces are given two thorough soakings with the solution, applied through a hose and nozzle held close to the wood. The liquid is held in a cylindrical container and is forced through the hole under an air pressure of from 20 to 60 lbs.

The work had continued throughout the war years, to be completed in 1923, and the Professor's prescription was in use throughout.

He continued his researches into the parasites of the Blow Fly in his own time, and on his own premises, during the summer; but at the end of the school term the family went on holiday.

> It must have been our first summer in Westbrook House – just left prep school and was due to go to Downside next term. And we all went on this holiday, down to Yealmpton, near Plymouth. I went with Father in

his car. Mother took the other two boys down by train. We had a most adventurous journey. Somewhere between Salisbury and Exeter – in wide open country – the car broke down. Father peered among the works and as far as I can remember came out with a bit of broken metal and said: I'll have to get this fixed at some blacksmith. There were plenty of blacksmiths in those days. So he walked off and there was quite a long wait. Eventually he came back and said: O well, here we are, fitted it and we drove off. And then we got to Exeter and for some extraordinary reason – I remember this very vividly, the car swerved round to the left, mounted the pavement and crashed into the shop window of a small shop. I don't know why at all. I don't think we were going terribly fast. I don't think he broke a tyre. But what happened I don't know. Anyway, there we were. The canvas hood was up. Showers of glass came down. And Father disappeared inside the shop. A long wait, but eventually he came out with the shopkeeper, both wreathed in smiles so the window must have been paid for. And this time we got to our destination safely. It did pretty well take the whole day. We started early in the morning, I remember.

It was a two-seater car of the usual kind in those days. It had a dickie seat. It was a fore-runner of those rounded bull-nosed Morrises. Father drove around in fast cars. He frequently had accidents going up and down the Bath Road and often ended up in the ditch. All the roads in those days seem to have been flanked by ditches on both sides inviting you to career into them. The car just toppled over. You could pull it out again quite easily and we boys thought it was the most frightful joke. It was very draughty travelling in the dickie and in one model I remember the engine was underneath. The further you went the hotter it got under your bottom. We had to stop every now and again to let the engine cool and had to remember to pour water into the radiator when it had all boiled out.

A nephew on his wife's side, Gerald Lewton-Brain, possibly one of the two boys who went to Yealmpton by train, made the Professor's acquaintance at about this time.

I have been trying to get some sort of order into my spasmodic memories of my Uncle Harold. The general impression is – brilliant but erratic. Certainly he was fascinating to a ten to fourteen year old; quite unlike one's more predictable uncles. One remembers roaring down the (then) Bath Road in a D.F.P. Sports car with six of us children in it, two in the front, two on the turned back hood, two on the dickie seat. There was a pleasant holiday in Southwold where he dealt with the death watch beetle in the splendid Perpendicular-style church. He had devised a simple but effective fly trap (I have used it myself) in Mesopotamia – an inverted flower pot on a jam jar with a residue of jam.

The Professor's Report on 'The Control of the Blow-fly' is dated the 3rd of October 1919. It is as lucid as ever.

> Speaking broadly, the blow-fly plague of Australia is due to an enormous multiplication of a few species of *Lucilia*, *Calliphora*, etc., due to the fact that there are not in Australia the controls that check them elsewhere. Seeing that *Lucilia sericata* and *Calliphora erythrocephala* are among the Australian species, it has seemed likely that an investigation of the controls of these and allied species in England would indicate natural checks likely to be effective in Australia.

He then lists five natural controls, apart from climate and food, all of which he is attempting to breed, with the intention of exporting them to Australia. 'Why should these not also control the Australian species?'

Towards the end of his Report, he concludes that it is not really known what flies (i) attack sheep primarily and (ii) live in attacked wool.

'In one publication Froggatt definitely heads the article "The Sheep Maggot Fly" (*Calliphora rufifacies*) but then explains it is not the one attacking sheep; in the Prize Essay published by Cooper's, Froggatt says "All our typical blow-flies belong to the same genus *Calliphora*."'

Finally the Professor says:

The work at present in progress:
1. To work out the habits and life histories of these insects.
2. To accumulate a stock of information.
3. To determine exactly how to transmit them.

The Report was then despatched to Australia, presumably to the Advisory Council, where it became the subject of a fierce debate.

Meanwhile, an assurance came that the recommendations of the Professor's Memorandum of the 15th of January 1918 had at last been put into operation by the wheat-men. Under the title 'War on the Weevil', *The Times* reported, on the 27th of October:

> At the Royal Institution yesterday Professor H. Maxwell-Lefroy delighted his audience with a clear exposition of some of the chief types of destruction of food by insects and of the ways in which entomologists were helping to solve the problems. A matter which had become very grave during the war, he said, was the destruction of wheat by weevil, the larvae of a number of species of harmless beetles. On account of the lack of transport, immense quantities of wheat had been held up in Australia. When the 1918 crop was coming in, there were already 220 million bushels awaiting shipment.
>
> Grain could be subjected to a temperature of 159 deg. Fahrenheit without suffering injury, and they found that a temperature of 145 deg. applied for three minutes killed anything. One machine of the type now being used could destroy the insects and clean 20,000 bushels of wheat a day. They got a bucketful of weevils in two minutes. Up to the present no use for the insects had been found, but he thought that their fat might be used for soap-making. In a letter just received from Australia it was stated that the system was a brilliant success, and that criticism had been completely silenced.

'A Correspondent', in the same issue of *The Times*, informs us:

> Heavily infected wheat of the 1916–17 crop, rapidly becoming worthless and quite unfit to export, was treated in March, 1918, by the method suggested, and was then stacked in Sydney and remained free from weevil until September, 1918, when it was sold at the top price of 57s.9d. a bushel. The whole of the [Wheat] Commission's wheat is now treated before shipment. Nine plants are at work treating five and a half million bushels per month at a total cost of 3½d. the bushel.

In a masterpiece of understatement, he concludes: 'Professor Lefroy found that the situation was complicated. There was overlapping of authority.'

On the 16th of November, the Professor returned to a previous hobby, that of writing letters to *The Times* himself. On this occasion, however, he was obliged to submit it to the Rector first, for his approval.

It will be a benefit to the Empire if you will give publicity to the fact that there is a suddenly increased demand for trained entomologists for agricultural services, in medical, veterinary and sanitary services, and with planting companies. If this cannot be filled from this country the men required will be sought in America. And while the total number of trained men required is not enormous, there is here a very good opening for those who have a biological training and who can undergo a year's training in entomology. The majority of posts are in government service and are reasonably well paid, with much active out-door life. We have been content to train five or six a year in the past, which was about the number needed. Many more will be needed now, and it is an opportunity particularly well suited to demobilized officers, even if they are in some respects physically disabled. It is certain that there are men who have had a biological training and who are not aware of the possibilities and it will be a great pity if the services concerned have to seek trained men elsewhere. May I also point out that the careers there will be in this subject for boys who have a natural aptitude for natural history and for insects; at present these boys are directed to less congenial careers because their parents are ignorant of the possibilities here offered.

This letter, shorn of all personality and much of its information, appeared in *The Times* of the 20th of November, under the signature of Sir Alfred Keogh. 'It has been urged upon me that public attention should be drawn to this matter, and I therefore venture to attempt the task.'

The original letter, informal, enthusiastic and with its references to America, to demobilized officers, the physically disabled, planting companies and outdoor life, was reduced to dust and ashes. Nevertheless, it provoked a leading article in *The Times* on the day it appeared, and gave rise to a subsequent correspondence in which the Professor did not take part and in which he had no mention.

On the 21st of November, the Prime Minister's Department in Melbourne cabled the Australian High Commission in London: 'It is not desired Professor Lefroy take any action re shipment of parasites or visit of his assistant until information received – see my cable 29 Oct.'

It had in fact already been arranged that the Professor's chief assistant in this experimental work should accompany the shipment on the voyage, on one of the Commonwealth cargo boats. This was now delayed and, as the result of a Memo of the 23rd of December, from the Entomologist to the Government of Queensland to the Advisory Council, was postponed indefinitely.

A correspondence had been carrying on in *The Times* on the subject of: 'Where do Flies go in the Wintertime? Do they go to Gay Paree?', the first two lines of a popular song of the moment. Temporarily abandoning his sense of humour, or perhaps with his tongue firmly in his cheek, the Professor wrote a letter which they published on the 18th of December.

> The letters on this subject appearing in your columns have surprised myself and others who thought the facts were really more widely known. We have bred *Musca domestica* continuously here since September 1915, winter and summer; if the temperature goes down the fly lives over in any stage but cannot do so long in the adult or egg stage; it will apparently live indefinitely as a larva or pupa if kept cold. If at any time the temperature goes up, flies will come out and lay eggs. The same takes place near London in large aggregations of waste, such as the municipal dumps, and I have obtained *Musca domestica* in all stages in mild weather in December by digging in a large dump. In the same way, adult flies as well as eggs, larvae and pupae, can be got by searching in large manure heaps, but as these cool down unless continuously added to, one finds that the flies are usually only found as larvae and pupae in the ground about a foot below the surface and away from the heap. Given a warm spell, flies will emerge and will enter houses at any time, but flies will not live over the whole winter in warm places, because if warm they must breed.
>
> The above are the facts, but it may be said that I do not know *Musca* from *Stomoxys*, *Pollenia*, and others, so I may refer to the published work of R.H. Hutchinson, in the *Journal of Agricultural Research*, Washington. He says:
>
> > 'In the latitude of Washington, D.C., the horsefly may over-winter in two ways: (i) by continued breeding in warm places where food and media for deposition are available; and (ii) in the larvae and pupa stages in or under large manure heaps.' (15 April 1918)

In view of the apparent success of his Exhibition at the Zoo in 1915, he was justified in being surprised and, although he does not say so, disappointed. The sombre note is sounded once again: '...it may be said that I do not know...' is followed by a reference to another authority.

The barrage of adverse criticism from Australia, which continued unabated, and the apparent lack of approval from Sir Alfred Keogh, may well have started to undermine his self-confidence.

CHAPTER XIX

Early in 1920 the Professor resigned his Curatorship of the Insect House at the London Zoo. It was an honorary and administrative post, but he retained his practical interest in the insects.

> I remember once going with my father to deliver a working ants' nest to the Insect House at the London Zoo. I sat in the back of the car with a large box and there were tubes with ants running up and down them. I was terrified that a sudden jerk would upset them all over the floor and I would be covered with ants. And I was once given a box of stick insects to be delivered. I remember sticking them all on artificial trees.

The Plumage Bill, dropped in 1914 on the outbreak of war, was now introduced for its first reading into the House of Lords, under the title Importation of Plumage (Prohibition) Bill. Prohibition laws already existed in certain other countries, the United States, Australia and India in particular, but London was the greatest feather market in the world, annually importing some thirty-five million skins.

It was the wholesale quality of the proposed bill, the disagreeable scent of blanket legislation, which aroused the Professor's antagonism and dislike; but it was as an individual, rather than an entomologist, that he wrote this letter to *The Times*:

I represent no interest whatever…As I see the question, the trade in plumage is large, involves many workers in London and Paris, besides big interests in ostrich farming, etc. There are birds nearing extinction whose slaughter and use should be absolutely prohibited; there are others (e.g. the parakeet in India) whose destruction and export would be a benefit to India; there are some birds (e.g. the egret) which can be farmed and the feathers obtained without any cruelty, and a Plumage Bill could be drafted which would really protect rare birds, economically develop the cultivation of egrets, etc., and interfere as little as possible with trade and with our foreign relations (especially with France).

Unfortunately this Bill protects nothing. With our usual national hypocrisy, we will not commit the cruelty ourselves, but neither will we stop the cruelty effectually, for just as many albatrosses, egrets, etc., will be killed, after this Bill is passed, only instead of coming to London direct they will go to France or Amsterdam; and the proposed action, whereby certain species were secured total protection and others were developed for the industry, will be prevented.

There is also a little savour of 'pussyfoot' in this Bill. One man is drunk, therefore we must all be dry. A few women get nerves from cigarettes, therefore America must not smoke! There is some cruelty in egret hunting, therefore all plumage, except ostrich, is to be banned!

A little common sense would be useful. Do the members of the Royal Society for the Protection of Birds never eat spring chicken? And is this not as cruel as egret hunting? It is to be hoped that this Bill will not be passed on the crest of a wave of silly sentimentality and truly British hypocrisy. That which is wrong in the business is easily put right; but the Bill as at present drafted, will do a great deal of harm to a section of trade and industry without righting any wrong at all.

Dated the 17th of March, from Westbrook House, Heston, this letter appeared on the 20th of March and seems to have enraged practically everyone.

Mr W.P. Pycraft, from the Museum of Natural History, on the 23rd of March:

…Professor H.M. Lefroy begins an attack on the new Plumage Bill… which is, from first to last, a tissue of half truths. That a man of science should so airily fling aside the first principles of scientific discussion to support a traffic which entails an appalling waste of life of the highest importance to the biologists of today, and of tomorrow, would be incredible but for the evidence set out over his own signature...The Plumage Bill is not primarily concerned with cruelty...[It] is to save birds being swiftly reduced by the demands of the millinery trade to the verge of extinction...The Bill's opponents are adopting a sordid and callous policy.

Mr H.H. Johnston, on the 24th of March:

...Chief reason is the economic value of birds being killed for the decoration of women's hats and busts – for no useful purpose whatsoever... for the adornment of parasitic, brainless women, better dead...The specious argument that the closing of Great Britain for the sale of this type of plumage will throw this iniquitous trade into the ports of Holland and France counts for nothing... [the trade] is only for the benefit of those outlaws of humanity, the Levantine plumage traders... Let us join the United States in setting an example to the civilised world.

Mr Aubyn Trevor-Battye, of the Council of the Zoological Society, the British Ornithologists' Union and the Royal Society for the Protection of Birds, on the 24th of March:

I am afraid my friend, Professor Lefroy, has gone into print before getting properly hold of his facts... he must... do the ornithologists the courtesy to concede that they may be actuated not by 'silly sentimentality' but rather by the scientific desire to preserve from decimation or extinction what still remains of the world's most interesting and remarkable ornithological fauna. If, say, the birds of paradise of New Guinea, the lyrebirds of Australia and others could have been adequately protected by the special legislation he suggests, the Bill would have been so framed...The professor's 'spring chicken' pleasantry would... better apply were we to kill our cocks and hens and let chicks starve!

The Chairman of the RSPB, Mr Montagu Sharp, on the 25th of March:

The time has passed when the wholesome sentiment of a nation against useless, cruel, and mischievous destruction of life can be pushed aside by a jibe, or by an appeal to commercial profit or a bid for a chuckle by the man in the street...The ostrich farmers of South Africa *desire* the measure. Statistics have shown that labour employed on 'fancy' feathers is seasonal and ill-paid, and workers numerically negligible... Finally, we are asked is not the eating of spring chickens as cruel as the hunting of egrets? The answer is in the negative.

But the Professor was not alone. Dr J.E. Duerden, of the Royal Colonial Institute, wrote:

> There is a dearth of facts, and sentiment in plenty. It is strange to find ostriches exempt from provisions of the Bill. Investigations might show that other plumage industries could be built up. Have steps been taken in the country of origin to prevent cruelty? The RSPB should attack the problem at the fountainhead instead of supporting legislation to make the world more dull and drab.

The Editorial Director of the National Trade Press wrote to say that the seven hundred people employed in the trade could find no other work. The MP for Finsbury had received petitions signed by 1,100 employees in his constituency and asked, on the 1st of May, for the second reading of the Bill to be postponed for six months.

On the 8th of June a public demonstration was held, presided over by Colonel Archer-Shee, the MP for Finsbury, and attended by Dr J.E. Duerden, Professor of Zoology at Rhodes University in South Africa, and Professor H.M. Lefroy. The procession was headed by the band of the London Rifle Brigade, from Charterhouse Square to the Farringdon Street Memorial Hall.

The French Government instructed their Ambassador to inform the British Government of the difficulties which would be created for the French trade by the Plumage Bill.

On the 5th of July, Sir Charles Hobhouse himself, he who had fought for the introduction of the Bill in 1914, wrote to *The Times*:

> In 1914 practically the whole trade was in the hands of foreign buyers who came to England for periodic sales and took nearly the whole trade to the Continent for manufacture and distribution. Members of the House of Commons who abstain from the Standing Committee are working in the interests of foreigners.

On the 5th of May of the following year, *The Times* ran a leading article, to the effect that 'the Bill must be made law'. On the next day, Colonel Archer-Shee introduced an amendment to the Bill, to permit the importation of feathers of birds killed abroad as pests. This was thrown out, as were fourteen other amendments, some of them 'frivolous'; and the second reading of the Bill was passed in the House of Lords.

In Lord Buckmaster's words: 'All the cruelties to which the birds were subjected were just to ease the ache of a woman's vanity, and to pay tribute to the deity of fashion, whom many worshipped and all despised.'

The deity of fashion, however, was on the side of the birds. Queen Mary had already eschewed the wearing of aigrettes and fancy plumes for herself. When her newly married daughter-in-law, the Duchess of York, drove from Buckingham Palace to Waterloo Station, in an open carriage on the first stage of her honeymoon on the 26th of April 1923, she wore a very simple hat of velvet, ornamented at one side with a small bunch of ostrich feather tips.

It was a forerunner of the cloche hat, to make its triumphant appearance in the following year, and to dominate the headgear of the 'woman in the street' for nearly ten years. It was a kind of felt helmet, pulled down to the eyebrows, rarely ornamented with anything more elaborate than a broad band of ribbon or a cluster of *appliquéd* flowers. Made in straw, velvet, brocade and various other intricately woven materials, it needed little decoration. Ostrich feathers, alone, continued to be worn at Court and in the ballroom. Some of the largest feather fans ever known to high fashion date from this time.

The Professor never again attempted to introduce a 'pleasantry' into the solemn letter columns of *The Times*. He is recorded as still suffering from neurasthenia in April, but he was able to give a lecture on the 16th of that month of which, unfortunately, only an abstract remains.

The Menace of Man's Dispersal of Insect Pests

In the past destructive insects have been carried about the world on plants and in merchandise; to England have come such pests as codlin moth of apple, woolly aphis of apple, hessian fly of wheat, black currant mite and the white fly of tomato. Elsewhere far more destructive pests have been carried, such as Mexican boll weevil, and pink boll worm of cotton, Colorado beetle, gipsy moth, corn moth, fluted scale, Hawaiian cane fly, San Jose scale, and others; these are pests of the very first magnitude whose effects on crops amount to millions sterling. The future menace is greater owing to:

1. Increased railway communications provided by the Channel tunnel, Gibraltar tunnel, the Cairo–Baghdad link (completed), and presently the Basrah–Karachi, the India–Burma and Burma–China linking up.
2. The aeroplane, which bridges sea-routes at present only covered by boats.

The construction of aeroplanes and airships allows them to carry insects; and whereas trains and boats start from stations and docks in towns, remote from field and orchard, planes and airships get up from fields and come down again in fields, thereby directly transmitting the crop pest.

Short cuts bridged by aircraft are: Africa–Brazil: Bombay–Africa: Peshawar–Turkestan: Calcutta–Rangoon–Bangkok: Japan–China: Philippine Islands–Borneo–India: Cairo-Baghdad–Karachi: Java–Queensland: Italy–Tripoli: Florida–Cuba–Yucatan.

In addition to carrying crop pests the aircraft will make possible the rapid transmission of the tse-tse flies, mosquitoes with yellow fever and malaria, lice with typhus, trench fever and relapsing fever; and this will be used as a war measure in future wars. Not only diseases, but virulent pests of crops, such as the boll worms, cane borers, rubber, tea and coffee pests will be spread from one area to another as an offensive measure.

It was not a public lecture. It was given at the weekly evening meeting of the Royal Institution and it sounds an uncomfortably prophetic note. Not all these newly opened routes provided the way for insect introductions of epidemic proportions; but the fact that the possibility had been foreseen as early as this may well have prevented it from becoming a probability.

It was, however, one of the Professor's greatest pre-occupations at that time. Sir Peter Chalmers Mitchell, then the Secretary of the Zoological Society, undertook a 'golden journey', first by the Orient Express to Trieste, then by ship to Egypt and then by 'plane down the East Coast of Africa. He records, in his book *My Fill of Days* (Faber, 1936):

> Before leaving London my friend Maxwell Lefroy had reminded me that many of the most serious insect pests had been spread by human agency. Insects, perhaps harmless in their native homes, might turn into pests when transferred to new conditions, and in fact sometimes had done so, and insects known to be noxious had spread to new territories along trade routes. The cockroach had come with shipping to Europe, the fleas of ship rats had brought plague, the Colorado beetle, once a harmless feeder on wild plants, had devastated potato crops in the United States and had come to Europe with potatoes. Lefroy had gone over the plane with me in London and had shown me every nook in which insects might lurk and had provided me with tubes and preservatives, so that specimens might be brought back for him to identify. He hoped by that method to get some idea as to how far air transport might be a danger by its swift transport of insects.

Although Sir Peter, in the event, did not find any insects, he did look. He was aware of the danger.

In June, the first post-war Imperial Entomological Conference was held, in London.

It began with a discussion on the legislation required to deal with plant pests in the British Empire. There was general agreement that more trained men were needed to supervise and carry out the legislation, and to give the public more information about the role and value of entomology. The war had proved, beyond question, its importance both as a study and, for instance, in dealing with the spread of malaria and the various fevers carried by lice.

On the second day of the meeting, the Professor read a paper on 'The Education of Economic Entomologists' and an energetic debate then followed.

Replying to various critics, the Professor said again that one training could not produce both specialists and administrators, that special scientific and full agricultural training would take too long. There was a need to steer between the two. The Chairman diplomatically summed up by saying that it was the man, and not the system, that counted.

Opinions inevitably varied. One was that an entomologist's education should be based on pure science, another demanded high honours in agriculture. The representative from Australia said that a four-year course had been devised, with one year's practical work, and that economic entomology – taught by Mr W.W. Froggatt – was included; but he considered that this general training in agricultural science was not sufficient and hoped for some guidance from the Conference.

Details of training methods in the United States were given, broadly based on agriculture, and other speakers stressed the importance of biology, botany and zoology. The speaker from Dublin said it was impossible to draw a line between pure and applied science and that a thorough training in both physics and chemistry was required. The representative from the West Indies said that plant physiology and mycology were necessary studies, and the speaker from Wye College said that agriculture, horticulture, mycology, plant physiology and some veterinary knowledge were desirable.

Mr C.F.C. Beeson, who had accompanied the Professor to Mesopotamia and who was now representing India, gave some details of the training of the forest entomologists in India. Their grounding in science was received in England, but the fieldwork could only be done in India as part of a team with, for instance, both botanists and mycologists.

At their next meeting, under the chairmanship of Sir Daniel Morris, with whom the Professor had originally worked in the West Indies, the discussion was largely about the resistance of plants to attack by insects. Mr H.A. Ballou, from the West Indies, summed up by saying: 'Our task is to produce healthy plants which would thus be enabled to hold their own against insects.'

At the last meeting, on the 9th of June, the representative from Trinidad spoke about 'Artificial versus Natural Methods of Control of Insect Pests', and the subsequent discussion, once more, produced many different points of view. The diplomatic Chairman, Professor R. Newstead, FRS, summed up by saying that, while the introduction of natural enemies was advisable, care was needed in their selection so that no crops would be endangered.

What is absolutely clear from all these discussions is that the profession of economic entomologist which, twenty-one years previously, had had no meaning whatsoever, was now being taken very seriously indeed throughout the British Empire.

There can be no doubt that the Professor had contributed largely to this fact. A Memorandum on the work of the Imperial Bureau of Entomology in this year records that the ten entomologists sent to the United States on Carnegie Grants had all completed their training and were now at work, as economic entomologists, in various parts of the Empire. The size of their contribution, the value of that work, cannot possibly be calculated.

CHAPTER XX

In 1920 the Professor's mother died, in Dorset, as did Mr F.M. Howlett, in India. The family was still living comfortably at Heston and that summer seems to have been spent there. The Professor's son was to be thirteen in that year.

Perhaps because of the grievous loss of two children in early childhood, my father was extremely fond of children, and they invariably took to him. I was always encouraged to invite boys of my own age to spend the summer at Westbook House, with its large garden and tennis court. But Heston was only a small village in those days and female society largely comprised elderly married women and widows. The only girl I ever met was the daughter of General and Mrs. Caddell who, with her brother, were the only other young people in the village whom it was considered socially acceptable for me to meet. So I grew up in an almost monastic environment.

One big advantage was the turn-table dining table...We had a constant battle with the butler about whether it was to be billiards or eating. He was a lugubrious, impassive man. He thought us very frivolous.

My father's total dedication to, and absorption in, his crusade against the dangers to mankind posed by malevolent insect species tended to obscure the warmth, kindliness and generosity of his personal character. He was a shy man who became transfigured when his enthusiasm for his latest interest took hold, all the barriers came down and he was once again the eager schoolboy of shining eyes and gesticulating hands, whilst tears of pure enjoyment would run down his cheeks. I never saw him angry. When he was amused his eyes would screw up and overfill with tears and he would mop them with his handkerchief, still shaking with amusement.

And then there were two sad occasions. On the first one he rather sheepishly unwrapped a bicycle. Well, I didn't need a bicycle – my legs would take me around then. And I had no premonition that anything like this was coming. I took it rather grudgingly and wheeled it off. I'm sure it was probably intended as a lovely surprise, no doubt about that, but he didn't know enough about me. I don't think any of the other boys had bikes – we didn't have far to go. I got fond of it in the end. But if only he'd said 'Look here, do you want a bike?' or something. Perhaps he'd expected me to ask for a bike. I don't know.

The cricket bat was the other one. I think he suddenly thought 'Well, my boy's keen on cricket. I'd better do something for him.' So without any consultation he bought me a cricket bat. I wanted one autographed by J.B. Hobbs. I remember him coming in one evening with some long object wrapped up in brown paper and he proceeded to unwrap this like an Egyptian mummy you might say. And it slowly revealed – ooh, a cricket bat. And when he got it down I leapt on it but when I tried to use it the handle nearly got to the bottom of my chin. Far too big for me. So I just flung the thing down and stormed out. I've never been good at hiding my emotions. It was the wrong make. If only he'd asked me. But he thought one cricket bat was like another. I think he was upset and bewildered rather than angry.

Continuing his crusade, particularly against the housefly, the Professor delivered a lecture on 'Insect Enemies of Man' in Margate, as reported in *The Times* of the 15th of September. His audience was attending the 33rd annual conference of the Sanitary Inspectors' Association and it is sobering to discover that he found it necessary to outline the life history of the housefly to them, and to explain how the flies polluted both milk and food. 'There was direct proof that such diseases as summer diarrhoea in infants, enteric, typhoid and paratyphoid, dysentery, cholera, and ophthalmia were transmitted by flies.'

After speaking about fleas and lice, and mentioning the diseases that they carried, he went on once more to outline his newest fear, the 'dispersal of insect pests as a result of aerial communication with distant lands'.

> We do not want, for instance, cholera brought direct from Africa to an aerodrome outside London at a time when there were abundant flies to spread infection; nor did we want an airman from, say, Holland to come with a fur-coat full of typhus-infested lice. One of the worst disease-carriers of the tropics, not normally found in England, was reported breeding near a London aerodrome last year. Another phase was the use of insects in warfare. In order to spread cholera, it was not necessary to poison wells. Releasing flies fed on a culture would spread the infection. It would be easy for the agent of a country hostile to us to liberate thousands of disease-carrying flies at a time when our own flies were abundant. One continental country would hesitate to infect another for fear of the plague spreading back to themselves, but with an island like ours, or with a continent as vast as America, the use of this weapon is obvious.

Teaching now became the most important part of his life. He was in fact running the only course in entomology in the country and it is clear that he was an able and popular lecturer.

One of his pupils, one of at least three women, took entomology as a special subject in Zoological Honours from Bedford College:

> Certainly Lefroy was able to communicate his enthusiasm to his students. Field expeditions were always fully attended, as were his lectures. Since classes were small he knew all his students by name and would sometimes hold up the class while waiting for an habitual late riser.
>
> He wasn't a theoretical lecturer. He spoke rapidly and in detail about the insects on the syllabus, occasionally punctuating the flow with a remark about Indian life. Students who had fallen asleep at their desks, often in darkness, in other class-rooms while the lecturer's voice droned on and light from the epidiascope flickered on the wall, were wide awake during Lefroy's lectures. His field trips were a revelation. He taught us to see, to look, and to find. He could be withering, not in words but with a look, if one made a mistake.
>
> He didn't particularly use his students to help with his research, as others did – Miss Olive Lodge, Miss Cheesman. We were left very much to ourselves. There was no tutorial system and we took our Finals in November.

In a separate letter, written in 1980, the same student remarks: 'We much enjoyed the course & loved our Prof. Lefroy, & I still have all my notes, records & drawings done under and for him & his signature on the fly-leaf.'

The late riser in question, Mr H.C.F. Newton, wrote in a letter: 'I was never an early riser. He would ask at lecture time, ten o'clock, "Is Newton here yet?" And if I was, "Then we will begin the lecture."'

The Professor's principal recommendation to aspiring entomologists was a simple one: 'An absolute essential is an innate love of the subject; without it the life is intolerable.'

He issued to his students a condensed classification of insects and, interestingly enough, commercial sales catalogues of various pesticides, but the first textbook seems to have been *Farm and Garden Insects* by William Somerville, published by Macmillan in 1897. It contained a short general introduction to entomology and an account of the identification, life history, prevention and eradication of such insects as might be expected, either annually or periodically, to give trouble to the farmer or the gardener.

Pests to fruit and forest trees were not included, but there were, for instance, ten chapters on insects injurious to various crops and vegetables, their physical descriptions and life history and all preventative and remedial measures. It was clear and concise, with sensible sub-headings and forty-six excellent line drawings.

It was during this time that my father's enthusiasm for all manner of projects reached its peak: many had no connection with entomology and many of our visitors, I suspect, had only one objective, namely to extract money from this kindly, gullible scientist for *their* pet projects. He got very interested in colloids, which he explained to us was a suspension of small drops of something in a fluid base. At one time he conceived the idea of making non-flammable petrol in the form of a colloid but this idea didn't take off. We thought it a frightful joke. On every conceivable occasion we would say 'Colloid the thing' until Father said 'That's enough'. But my mother remained constantly on guard lest my father's enthusiasm would be carried to the point of squandering money on new ideas that had little prospect of commercial success.

He was not particular about his dress although not to the point of eccentricity. Shoe laces were properly tied and if trousers and jacket became baggy through assorted objects being constantly thrust into pockets that was no more than would be expected of a Professor. Nor would the appellation 'absent-minded' fit.

A favourite saying of Father's when he was in a good mood:

'Beer brings gladness, don't forget
Water only makes you wet.'

I don't recall the origin of this ditty. Might have been Germany or Cambridge. Or he could have made it up himself.

One of the great surprises to visitors to Westbrook House must have been to hear all the latest jazz records being played on a large wind-up His Master's Voice gramophone. They arrived unsolicited from the Columbia Gramophone Company and the Gramophone Company – later to merge and form EMI – both of whom had almost certainly asked the Professor's advice about lac, a vital ingredient of the shellac with which all their records were coated.

Lac, also an important part of lacquer, alone among the resins is an animal product. The Professor had cultivated it at Pusa, though mostly for demonstration purposes, and again in conjunction with the Forests Department in 1911–12, with a view to forming a peasant industry. The insects concerned, *Coccus lacca*, attach themselves to the young shoots of various mature trees, by means of a long 'beak', in November. They exude a resinous secretion to form cocoons and these, hundreds and thousands of tiny insects joined together, make a continuous hard layer which is harvested as 'stick lac'. This is most profitably done in June and November.

The trees on which the lac insects live are all native to southern Asia, the peepul or bo-tree (*Ficus religiosa*), the Flame of the Forest (*Butea frondosa*), the Indian Jujube (*Zizyphus jujuba*), the Rain Tree or Saman (*Enterolobium saman*) and the Mango, and the principal Empire sources of lac at the time were Bengal, Assam and the Pegu district of Burma.

The trees were all large forest trees, not in plantations, and so the industry had to remain a peasant industry, based on cheap and plentiful labour.

The Lac Insect had originally been cultivated for the red dye produced by the females, who far outnumber the males, the ovary being a red sac. Shellac was then the by-product but the position was now reversed, and the gramophone companies were looking for enormous quantities of shellac all the year round.

At the Imperial Entomological Conference in 1920 a paper was read by Mahdi Hassan 'on the cultivation of lac from a physiological point of view', and the Professor had certainly heard it. It showed that the production of lac increased only after a forest fire. Clearly this course of action was too desperate to be taken in order to meet the demands of the gramophone companies; but the Professor could advise them how to deal with their suppliers, and how to find new ones. He was in regular correspondence with entomologists in India. Meanwhile, the records continued to arrive.

The summer of 1921 was long, and hot. An interview with the Professor was published in *The Times* on the 9th of September under the title 'Insect plague' – 'Triple broods due to drought' – 'A mosquito mystery'.

The prolonged drought had had an extraordinary effect on insect life. The Codlin Moth, great enemy of apple trees, had produced three broods instead of the more usual two, or one in a cold year.

The extreme heat had caused mosquitoes to breed more freely and houseflies had multiplied more rapidly than ever. Wasps, unable to find any liquid, had attacked the ripening fruit in August. '"I have even seen a wasp drinking from a tap this summer, a thing I have never seen before," said Professor Lefroy.'

Roadside weeds had been burned up, affecting the greenfly which normally fed on those weeds. The natural enemies of greenfly – the Ladybird Beetle, the Hoverfly, the Lace-wing – would therefore also be scarce in the following year. 'We can expect an enormous disturbance in the normal balance.'

The report concluded:

During this year there have been an abnormal number of deaths from either stings from wasps or bites of the brown mosquito (which is not a carrier of malaria in England), or from bites of unidentified flies. To some extent this is due to the fact that the hot and dry conditions have led these insects to attack man more freely, but we are ignorant about why the bite of a harmless brown mosquito can cause death within two to three days. It is extraordinary that coroners can pass verdicts of 'Accidental Death' without emphasising the need of investigation into the actual cause of death. This is a subject which undoubtedly requires investigation, and yet it is frequently tacitly accepted as the cause of death.

One of the more bizarre contacts ever made by the Professor took place at this time. It was with the College of Pestology. This seems to have been an organisation with highly praiseworthy aims, an impressive list of Vice-Presidents, very little basic funding and no permanent address.

At some time, variously stated as 1921 and 1924 – for the College, entirely in keeping with its faintly evanescent character, has no archives – the Professor became Chairman of its Applied Biology Panel. This post appears to have carried with it no duties, and quite certainly no remuneration. The Professor was apparently simply 'lending his name'. He was quite possibly the only entomologist at that time whose name was known to the general public.

The College seems to have been successor to the Vermin Repression Society. This was founded about 1905 by James Crichton-Browne, Treasurer of the Royal Institution, and William Simpson, then occupying the Chair of Hygiene at King's College, London. The Society did much excellent work and was largely responsible for the passing of the Rats and Mice (Destruction) Act, by which local authorities became liable for the elimination of these vermin.

On the 10th of January 1920, a luncheon was held at the Connaught Rooms to celebrate the passing of this Act; and it was attended by the Parliamentary Secretary to the Ministry of Agriculture, Sir Arthur

Boscowen. He is on record as saying that the destruction caused by rats and mice in a single year was equal to the whole cost of the old age pension. Having achieved this, its initial aim, the Vermin Repression Society seems to have closed down.

By 1922 an Institute of Pestology, with an address at 29 Charing Cross Road, had come into existence. It had an MP as its President · and its Chairman was a certain Lieutenant Alfred E. Moore, who had become interested in vermin destruction during the War and who held a commission in the Territorial Army. The aims of this Institute were in every way admirable, being, among others:

1. To promote the study of the life history of disease-carrying animals, birds, insects and plants.
2. To promote the study of Economic Zoology, Bacteriology, Mycology, and kindred sciences, and to co-ordinate them into the cognate science of Pestology.
3. To promote the dignity, well-being and interests of all engaged in … the elimination of vermin.
4. To educate the public.

Possibly the use of the phrase 'the cognate science of Pestology' was an error here. The College, which followed the Institute, does not appear to have been taken very seriously by other experts at the time. The actual word 'pestology' was no part of the vocabulary of fully qualified entomologists or mycologists. The Institute did, however, publish two issues of a quarterly journal called *Pestology*, one in July and one in November, 1922.

The College of Pestology had its address at 52 Bedford Square, although the Bedford Estates have no record of this. Possibly they were sub-tenants. The Duke of Sutherland was its President, Sir Thomas Horder, the eminent surgeon, and the Hon. Henry Mond, the eminent banker, were Deputy Presidents, but the Treasurer, the Auditors and the Secretary were all Honorary. Membership cost one guinea, associate membership ten shillings and sixpence, and the Prospectus ran along these lines:

Would *you* allow *your* child to play on a grass plot lately the bed of a vermin-ridden tramp for example?

Would *you* willingly allow a flea from a cancerous or tuberculous person access to *your* children?

It is no use being squeamish in these matters, the evils exist and they have got to be tackled, and it is the College of Pestology's duty to tackle them. But unsupported work must fail.

It is not difficult to see that the Professor, with his great goodwill towards anyone trying to combat insect-borne diseases, would have agreed to support a project of this kind; but, in fact, there seems to have been nothing to support. Lectures, classes, public meetings, do not appear to have been held. Its excellent intentions never seem to have assumed a concrete form.

CHAPTER XXI

On the 10th of March 1922, *The Times* noted that the Professor had given his second lecture – they do not seem to have reported his first one – at the Royal Institution. It was entitled 'The balance of life in relation to insect pest control'.

> He said that the rate of increase of pests such as the blue-bottle, moths, greenfly, etc., was controlled not only by parasites, but by birds, toads, lizards and climate. When Man cut down a forest and planted something for his own use it upset the balance of life, and the control of pests by parasites was affected. One reason why the United States was suffering so much was because a great deal of land had not been cleared until recent times, and it took a very long time for the balance of life to reassert itself. Again, by growing crops, food was provided for pests that Nature would not provide.
>
> This country suffered less from pests than almost any other. The balance of life was due to the steady proportion of different kinds of crop. It was important not to upset that balance by introducing new crops. If sugar beet, for instance, was grown over large areas, then any insect which could feed on sugar beet would increase and multiply. But if a new crop must be grown, precautions must be taken to protect it. He expected that a hundred years hence there would be legislation whereby the balance of life could not be disturbed by anyone planting a large area with a new crop.

The reference to the United States was about the 'dust bowl' conditions which were just beginning to be serious and which were to cause many problems, and a great deal of misery, over the next fifteen to twenty years.

There is no comment on the Professor's health in the files of Imperial College for this year, from which we may hope that it had improved. Sir Alfred Keogh was succeeded as Rector by Sir Thomas Holland, a man with an extensive Indian background, who would, firstly, have known all about the Professor's achievements in India and, secondly, would have understood his instinctive dislike of all forms of bureaucratic control.

Sir Thomas, a geologist, went first to India in 1890 and, as a result of his exertions, a Chair of Geology was created at the Presidency College in Calcutta. He accepted the first Chair but resigned, leaving India for Manchester in 1909. In 1920 he returned to India as Commerce Member of the Viceroy's Executive Council, but resigned in 1921 after 'differences' with the Viceroy, Lord Reading. It seems probable that it was he who allowed the Professor the 'free hand' he had always required in his researches.

The Professor did have a social life outside his family but, if we are to judge by the condition of his evening dress, it was not very extensive, neither were his dinner engagements very frequent. His son records:

> I can recollect the flurry of excitement when he was once invited to dine by H.G. Wells and his ancient dress suit was eventually unearthed and dusted down; at the last moment a frantic search had to be launched for his white waistcoat and tie in which we boys joined excitedly and contributed (probably deliberately) to the prevailing confusion. At last he was properly 'assembled' and departed amidst cheers.

H.G. Wells, novelist, sociologist and historian, who had attended the Royal College of Science in South Kensington with the aid of grants and scholarships, published, in 1922, *A Short History of the World*.

They were still living at Westbrook House.

My father displayed his kindly and tolerant nature when I set up a chemical lab. in the conservatory adjoining the house. At Downside, where I was one of three boys doing science in Army Class, I got hold of some chemical manufacturers' catalogues, and using my father's name as reference, ordered chemicals of bright colours and exotic names. When the bills came in to Father he must have been quite astonished but only after he paid them did he call me in and tell me quite kindly that what I had done was wrong and had to stop. At that time he was totally absorbed in various researches and probably regarded my peccadillo as a minor diversion to be disposed of speedily and without fuss.

At this period also my father became interested in the control of mosquitoes and midges by destroying larvae in the water wherein they bred. This was done by spraying the surface of ponds and streams with a thin film of oil to which a toxic substance had been added. I remember posing for a photograph spraying a pond against malaria at General Caddell's house from a knapsack sprayer. And this appeared in *The Field*.

The British Broadcasting Company, as it was originally known, was founded in 1922. In the words of John Reith, it's first General Manager, in a broadcast made in November of the following year: 'We believe that in co-operation with our listeners we can bring into homes all that is best and most worth while in every department in human achievement, knowledge and endeavour.'

In their search for purveyors of knowledge, they received sympathetic and practical assistance from the directors of the South Kensington Museums, for instance, and inevitably they encountered the Professor. No one could have been, at that time or at any other, more anxious to share his knowledge with the general public and he was here offered an audience which no number of public lectures could possibly reach. On the 12th of February 1923, at nine o'clock in the evening, he gave a talk on 'The Death Watch Beetle', a topic much discussed as the repairs to Westminster Hall neared completion; on the 10th of March, at ten to eight, 'Where do flies go?' and on the 14th of July, at 9 p.m., 'The recent outbreak of flies'.

Miss Evelyn Cheesman, still working at Imperial College, made some broadcasts on Children's Hour at this time, which explains her following reference to Uncles and Aunts:

> A Talk was rather an ordeal because of the habit of Uncles and Aunts to pace the studio and give sudden ejaculations from different points. Another habit was suddenly to confront you with a notice – 'Faster, please', or 'A little slower', which always made me jump. We did not write scripts and therefore they sounded more spontaneous but concentration was all the more intense.

The Professor, however, did write his scripts, one of which, miraculously enough, has survived. Possibly as a result of his broadcast in February, in June the Professor received a letter from the Rt Hon. Sir Henry Norman, Bt MP, which may well have been typical of similar enquiries:

> My dear sir,
>
> May I ask you to be so good as to tell me if the accompanying grub, which has fallen from an old oak beam, is the true X. Tessellatum, of Westminster Hall fame?
>
> With many thanks, I am
> Yours faithfully
> Henry Norman

Sir Henry's country address was at Chiddingfold in Surrey and we are to suppose that that is where the grub was found; but the Professor's reply, sadly enough, is not known.

In 1922, a company called New Era films was started, ostensibly to market a war film by Bruce Woolf, but they also began to distribute short films previously made, on such subjects as *The Garden Spider* and *The Cuckoo*, which had found no takers in Wardour Street. A series called *Secrets of Nature* began in 1922. The Professor, at the beginning of the latter year was certainly involved in two of them, *The Tiger Beetle* and *The Wasp*. Several of these films can still be seen, at the National Film Archive.

Inspired by a war-time reading of Gilbert White's *Natural History of Selborne*, Bruce Woolf of British Instructional Films Co. decided to make short films about the insect world. The first, the life story of the garden spider, was made in 1919 by Charles Read, chosen for his interest in photographing insects. Read very quickly became fascinated and was cameraman for all the insect films in the series, *Secrets of Nature*.

Having made the films it was found hard to get them distributed until, from 1922, New Era Films succeeded in interesting cinema managers in them. Woolf enlisted the help of skilled naturalists, and cameramen, hitherto unable to tell a blackbird from a thrush, were engaged to interest people without special scientific knowledge in the world about them. The first five sets of six films were released in 1922, a second five sets in 1923, and so on. The series was an outstanding success, admired in Europe for editing and photography, and distributed also in the United States.

The Professor would have been delighted to share in the challenge of this new way of presenting the facts and the fascination of insects. Before his death he had completed work on *The Puss Moth*, in which it is shown that the heroic idea of carrying flags into battle was conceived long before mankind went to war.

Set 3 of the films released in 1922 included *The battle of the ants*, which was 'engineered by the Zoo', and showed a fight between rival nests. Mary Field, editor of the whole series 'Secrets of Nature', has written: 'It was about as easy to follow on the screen as a football match between several thousand players, with both sides wearing jerseys of the same pattern. Possibly the ants knew what they were doing, but *we* didn't.' Film-making at the Zoo was not allowed to interrupt public access to the galleries, and a crowd of curious onlookers was an additional exasperation for the camera-men trying to cope with actors – the insects – whose movements and behaviour could in no way be controlled. Lighting too was a problem. That the films were so successful is a great tribute to the good humour and patience of these early pioneers in natural history educational films, copies of which are at the National Film Archive.

On the 27th of July 1923, Westminster Hall was re-opened by King George V, accompanied by Queen Mary, and very shortly afterwards Edward Arnold published *A Manual of Entomology* by Harold Maxwell-Lefroy, illustrated with line drawings by L.N. Staniland, one of his more able pupils. In his Preface, dated from Heston, he said:

> This volume is based upon the lectures given as the second of three parts of a course occupying one year of full training in economic entomology. To compile in book form a complete entomology, apart from description of species, would occupy many years and fill many volumes. In lecturing one's attempt is to pick out what the student can know – essentials, and not details, are the requisite – and this volume attempts to select the usual ordinary facts about each group, which the student requires.
>
> The underlying idea of this book is best expressed as follows: Imagine seven entomologists in Piccadilly Circus, and that they see a beetle in the road. The systematist says, '*Carabus serodecim-punctata* Smith var. *Nigro-fasciata* Jones,' and his interest ends there. The morphologist says, 'Beetle, with undeveloped hypopharynx, dieroistic egg-tubes, etc., etc.,' and his interest ends. The collector says, 'Ordinary common variety, ten males and females in my collection,' and passes on. The Mendelist speculates, thinks back over literature of inheritance in *Carabidae*, and wishes he were back in his library. The evolutionist speculates also, as to the common ancestor of *Carabidae* and *Dermaptera*, as to whether the caraboid or scarbaeoid larva came first, and also passes on speculating. The bionomist says, 'Carabid, carnivorous, free living, no business to be here,' and the economic man says much the same, but wonders what he would do if an outbreak occurred in Piccadilly and he was called in to cope with it. It is the last two men that I attempt to interest.
>
> Illustrations are reduced to the barest minimum, as I do not believe in encouraging identification from pictures. Every student should work with a collection, and, when reading up a group, have actual specimens to examine and dissect.

He acknowledges the help given to him in preparing the text by seven students of the College, past and present.

Little seems to be known of the fate of this book, neither is it perfectly clear why, in that summer, Westbook House was given up.

We moved to Sherlies, Orpington, Kent, a spacious guest house in what was then open country. Here Father taught me to drive the Singer car. As I was still only sixteen we operated in a field.

The wireless broadcasts continued. On the 3rd of October, at ten past nine in the evening, he gave a talk called 'Insects and the World's Clothes'.

This is a talk about insects really, and especially about the way insects are going to decide for us, one of our most important questions – what we are all to wear.

Now, we are all taught that Man is the dominant creature of this earth; and we all know how important to us all are our clothes. But here come insects, which to some people are insignificant, but which are far more highly-developed than man and these insects, quite incidentally and without intent to hurt man merely in pursuit of their own aims and successes, are going to seriously affect man in what he wears.

Mostly, the world wants and uses long cotton and nearly all this comes from America…the Lancashire mills depend almost entirely on its production for their manufactured goods. But it is now a question how much cotton is going to be grown in America at all. An insect called the boll weevil is the factor in that question. It destroys so much of the crop that it is becoming hardly worth while to grow cotton at all.

The boll weevil is a small brown insect, about the size of a dried pea, which came into Mexico from South America, then spread into the United States and is now established all over the cotton growing areas. This little weevil flies and walks among the cotton plants. The female with her long beak eats a hole into the green fruit or 'boll' of the cotton plant and then lays an egg in the hole. This egg hatches into a soft white grub which eats its way further into the boll so that it can feed on the developing seeds. The grub destroys the seeds and so destroys the developing cotton. When the boll opens, instead of there being a large fluffy mass of cotton, there is only a mass of black and eaten seeds – nothing that can be picked and used.

…in practically all parts of the world there is another insect as voracious as the boll weevil of America. This is known as the pink boll worm and it is a caterpillar hatching from an egg laid by a moth on the boll. The caterpillar, like the boll weevil, also eats the seed of the boll, destroys the fibre and prevents the cotton being formed. In Egypt, this insect takes about one fifth of the crop; elsewhere it will take from a fifth to three quarters, depending on the conditions. And up to now no real method has been found of dealing with it. In 1917 this insect was found in America, but the Americans hope they have wiped it out. If they have not...[the farmer] will not grow cotton but will turn his attention to maize, tobacco, fodder crops, cattle, pigs etc., or whatever is not menaced by insects as destructive as these.

Man, in spite of his intelligence, his science, his so-called control of Nature, cannot devise a means of killing boll weevil which the cotton farmer will adopt. We all have free will and free thought and our intelligences do not necessarily run on similar lines, while the activities of these two insect species are confined to the simple lines organised by Nature, they succeed in affecting the enormous industry that uses cotton, the immense wealth that is tied up in handling cotton and the vast number of people who wear clothes made of cotton; while the civilised man with his highly trained brain rushes from one idea to another without success in an endeavour to stop these activities. It is humiliating, isn't it?

What then shall we all wear? Shall we eventually control the boll weevil and the boll worm and so get cheap cotton, or shall we find a new fibre? Will Nature win and compel us to make artificially some fibre, such as artificial silk, which is not at the mercy of insect ravages and which can be produced at a price where we can all use it? The next ten years will show whether man will control the insect, or whether the insect will devour our cotton and send us to seek substitutes. I think the insect will win!!!

Reviews of the New Era films *Secrets of Nature* now began to appear. The *Bioscope*, the principal magazine of the film industry, referred to them, in its issue of the 20th of September 1923, as 'unique nature studies, photographed by leading British cinematographers and edited by recognised authorities on the subjects dealt with.' 'No introduction is necessary for a series of pictures, which by sheer merit, have won a deserved reputation throughout the country...Apart from their intrinsic interest, the films differ from nearly every other series of nature pictures in that they are absolutely free from fakery.'

They offered a review of a film called *The Mayfly* – 'One of the transitions illustrated – the emergence of the fly from the pupa – is stated never previously to have been photographed' – in which the

Professor may have been involved, and one of *The Story of Westminster Hall*, in which he certainly was.

> Rather dissimilar from the rest of the series, this well-composed film has a certain historical interest. The pictures trace the story of Westminster Hall, illustrates its salient architectural features and vividly discloses the recent efforts to repair the havoc caused by the tiny death watch beetle in its ancient timbers. A good shot of the King reopening the Hall concludes the production.

At the end of November, The *Bioscope* again reviewed two of the Professor's films:

> *The Tiger Beetle*. Of more serious scientific interest is this very fine camera study of a ferocious insect, whose eerie transformations and murderous disposition are fully and intimately illustrated. The titling gives a great deal of information about the horrid creature, without making it dull or prosy.
>
> *The Wasp*. Here is another cleverly made insect study, providing a vivid and detailed close-up of Waspland. Many curious facts about the wasp are brought to light in an admirably edited film, which blends instruction with entertainment.

At this point, however, the Professor's health seems once more to have broken down. His son recalls:

> He'd had a preliminary shot of poison gas experimenting in his lab. It was Lewisite. Trichlor-phenyl-arsene. I happen to remember the formula. Shortly before he died he happened to ask me – I was reading chemistry – d'you know the formula of this stuff? and it happened that I did. It was some surplus stuff from the Army, left over from the war. It may have been from General Caddell that he obtained supplies. The War Office was only too glad to get rid of it and apparently he wanted to try killing flies with it. Well, he was an entomologist, not a chemist. Both Mother and General Caddell tried to dissuade him. At any rate, this was a mild one and Mother took him off to Madeira to recuperate. I was still at school and didn't know what was happening. It must have affected the lungs.

This probably occurred shortly after the Professor had completed his report on the Middle Temple Roof, the first part of which is dated the 2nd of October and the second the 11th of October. On the 30th of

November, the Professor received a cheque from the Middle Temple for £52.10s.0d, but it is uncertain whether this was a pre-payment for the whole fee or a substantial down payment. Possibly it paid for the trip to Madeira.

The Report itself is as concise and as clear as always. 'The result of this examination is that it has not been possible to definitely obtain a single living insect.'

> Flight holes in timber surfaces that were dressed with linseed oil and turps in about 1908, in 1922: these are quite definite: when dressing is put over existing flight holes, each hole gets a rounded lip, as the dressing dries on it gets filled up; but when a beetle emerges through dressing already applied, it makes a sharp, clear-cut definite hole which is quite unmistakeable. There is no doubt that beetles have emerged since the dressing was put on in 1922 and there are many cases of beetles emerging since the earlier dressing.

In conclusion, he says:

> To look at some of the timbers leads me to the idea of very serious and extensive damage; but careful examination very usually shows nothing more than superficial damage in really big timbers. I think this is a point to keep very clearly before one: one wonders whether the authorities who handled Westminster Hall still agree that any renovation was really necessary; for there, hardly any, if any, live insects were found and though selected timbers were superficially or even thoroughly attacked, the opening up of the roof truss by truss did not endorse the disastrous condition pictured by the preliminary superficial examination.

It was, however, decided to treat the timbers and, in Part II of the Report, the Professor recommends the following mixture:

Zinc or Barium Oleate	3 per cent
Cedar Wood Oil	3 " "
Soap	1 " "
Paraffin Wax	10 " "
Water	83 " "

> This is a drying cream, made up in water which will remain as a permanent protective coat: it is not a human poison and will not, in the course of centuries, dust out: and it is a definite poison.

The insurance company concerned wished to know how inflammable the mixture was. In a letter to Sir Aston Webb, the architect in charge, in the following February, the Professor added, as a comment on this recipe: 'I may point out that a similar film of Paraffin Wax, Soap and Cedar Wood Oil, without the Zinc Oleate, has been applied all over Westminster Hall. As the Zinc Oleate makes our mixture still more resistant to fire, we may assume that our mixture is safe.'

The Report suggests that the work could be done while other work is in progress and that it would take about thirty weeks. 'I think that not less than £1500 will be spent and not more than £2000.' The work was completed on the 11th of November in the following year.

CHAPTER **XXII**

One result of this connection with Sir Aston Webb was that, on the 13th of February, the Professor read a paper entitled 'The Treatment of the Death Watch Beetle in Timber Roofs' to the Royal Society of Arts under the Chairmanship of Sir Aston. From this, it emerges that, while the treatment recommended had been successful, there was still a lot to learn about the beetle itself.

How does the roof become infested? Why does the attack stop? How can you recognise an attack deep in an inaccessible structure? The way in which an attack commences is of great interest, and I offer you three conjectures; they are:
1. That the original timbers are infested when put in place
2. That at any time after construction the insect is brought in with renewal repairs, or fresh timber objects, such as floors, pews, etc.
3. The insect itself comes in.

We have, unfortunately, no knowledge of the third; beetles do fly and may come into buildings; but it is unlikely and ill accords with what we know of the beetle's habits... The next point is, why an attack ceases; it undoubtedly does cease without reference definitely to anything that has been done to stop it... Lastly, I must deal with one point, the evidence of attack in progress in timbers inaccessible for examination; there are two sources of evidence; one is the holes in the wood from which the beetles have emerged, and which are unmistakeable; the other is the absolutely characteristic oval flattened pellets of excreta, which may pour out of a big roof joist, and which indubitably prove the presence at some time of the beetle.

I do think this is a serious matter that should be properly dealt with by some competent public body, so as to secure continuity and uniformity; it is novel, experimental, and not as yet on an established basis of experienced practice; we shall not see the results of the treatments experimentally done; and if the many fine timber buildings are to remain it will only be if this menace is dealt with.

In the discussion which followed, it became clear that Sir Aston Webb was not without his critics. Sir Frank Baines spoke for very nearly as long as the Professor – the 'author' – finally stating he 'had visualised the possibility of dealing with structures in the future by again treating them with some perfect insecticide against *Xestobium tessellatum*, such as he hoped the author could invent'.

In the middle of the Lent Term, Downside was closed due to an epidemic of 'flu and all the boys were sent home.

My father was determined that I should not hang around idly. He had discovered the existence nearby of a moth-balled Army Camp run by a retired Sergeant Major to whom he decreed that I should report for an hour each day for 'disciplining'. This unexpectedly hard streak in Father's normally 'far away' detachment from my existence came as quite a shock. I protested and asked to be taught to ride instead. Father was adamant – the cost of riding lessons would have been prohibitive – so I had to submit. I soon found that 'disciplining' took the form of playing Badminton with the S.M. and being taught fencing, which I greatly enjoyed. My respect for Father's wisdom and judgment was greatly enhanced. But horse riding remained an unattainable dream.

He did not carry his best goods in the front window: you had to prise open the door, go inside and look around, something I did not quite succeed in doing, perhaps for lack of help. But that my father cared for me deeply I realised when at age sixteen I had to have my tonsils removed. Instead of the local hospital at Orpington the op. was done in a London Nursing Home. Anaesthetics were primitive – a mixture of ether and chloroform. My anaesthetist got the mixture wrong. When I awoke from the op. I saw my father sitting in a chair at the end of the bed wearing a look of deep concern – and was promptly violently sick! A poor way to say thank you.

In April, the Professor said goodbye to Evelyn Cheesman, his former assistant at the Insect House, pupil and fellow broadcaster, as she left on a journey to the South Pacific which was to last two years. She records that the Professor 'stressed that nobody could form any conception of insect life without visiting the tropics', which was her own view, 'and proposed to put one of his students in my place to hold the fort until my return'.

In June, *The Times* reported that the Professor had spoken at the Empire Textile Conference at Wembley. He had returned to his old contention that the Empire could be self-supporting for raw silk, mentioning the great opportunities for improvement that existed in India and Cyprus; but the home textile industry had neglected the needs of the silk trade and British firms now had to obtain their machinery from America and the Continent.

At some time during that summer, the Professor paid his only visit to Downside, not particularly to see his son but to negotiate with the headmaster, the formidable Abbot Trafford, about the fees. Downside is in Somerset, and was then on the Somerset and Dorset Railway. The station was Chilcompton, where the school train would be met by a fleet of coaches. For parents, who were tolerated but not encouraged, it was a long and inconvenient journey. There was a sort of guest house which had two or three bedrooms, but there was nowhere else to stay.

Well, we were having a cricket match and I was in the First Eleven. And I was in the Pavilion. Having got out. A boy hissed in my ear 'Your father wants to see you.' I got out of the Pavilion and there was Father behind. And he said 'O hullo, I want to see the headmaster.' Fortunately, the headmaster was watching the cricket match, too. So he came over to see Father. Well, the headmaster was an enormous tall man. I used to look on him as Doctor Fu Manchu. Pale grey eyes, you know. And there was my father, he wasn't looking his best, I was almost ashamed at introducing him, his hat on the back of his head, coat stuffed with papers, trousers looked as if they'd been slept in. What transpired afterwards was that he couldn't afford to go on paying my fees so he wanted to see the headmaster. And he anticipated rather a chilly reception. But not a bit of it. I stood by goggling, watching the scene. Headmaster and Father put their arms together. They walked up and down and seemed to be getting on like a house on fire. And I discovered later that Father had thought of taking me away from Downside at the end of that term. It was still too early to go to Cambridge, so what would have happened to me I don't know. Anyway he got on so well with headmaster that he waived my fees – in a sense I was given a cricket scholarship. Anyway they were substantially reduced. Only later did my mother help me to realise what financial sacrifices my father had made in order to give me of the best.

On the 2nd of July, the *Daily Mail* carried the headlines 'Secret of the Death Watch Beetle'. 'The experts at Imperial College, South Kensington, have just discovered how it manages to hide itself in old timber and destroy valuable building fabrics.'

They had purchased three tons of infested flooring from the church of Knatton, in Yorkshire, and had examined the beetle under the microscope. '"Now we know the life history of the beetle," said Professor Lefroy yesterday, "we are prepared to deal with it in a way it won't like. Churchwardens and others concerned with ancient buildings can confess their trouble to us and we can tell them what to do to end it."'

Letters were to be addressed directly to the Professor at Imperial College.

That summer Father, Mother, I and our Irish terrier, Bingo, went on holiday to Lowestoft. Earlier, Father had been convalescing in Madeira and most of the time he was content to sit in a deck-chair on the beach and play with the dog. I think Lowestoft was the time when I first started to get keen on painting. I used to potter around. And I had a brand-new camera given to me – so I amused myself all right. Father made no comment on my painting, but money if I wanted more. I used to leave sort of half finished canvasses lying about on chairs and he was very good about that. No complaint or anything. On the other hand he didn't offer advice. Perhaps he felt he wasn't qualified to. But in photography he did help me. Showed me how to do printing out in sunlight and developing. And there again he was completely generous with money. I think he was completely absorbed in his own work. He wasn't interested in painting. Photography I think he was a bit interested in – he'd done some. But all these hobbies were subordinated to his own work. Even 'cello playing. Things like that.

He'd received a summons from his old college, King's, to inspect the wooden framework of the roof so we all drove to Cambridge on a bright sunny morning. We established ourselves at the Bull Hotel for lunch. After lunch Father went to his assignment whilst Mother and I wandered around the adjacent colleges. I had my camera – a Vest Pocket Kodak – and nothing was safe from my wavering lens. When Father rejoined us and we began our homeward journey I recall that he was strangely subdued. He said nothing and I wondered why. Much later Mother revealed that his inspection of the roof had involved some precarious high level manoeuvring and although he had gained experience at Westminster Hall he had never been able to conquer his fear of heights.

There had by now been a *rapprochement* in the Lefroy family. The Professor's only sister, Kathleen, who had most vociferously objected to his Catholic marriage, had converted to Rome. She and her sister-in-law, also Kathleen, went together on pilgrimage to that holy city. It was Holy Year, Anno Santo, and her conversion involved her family. Of her five sons, two were to enter the priesthood.

At about the same time, the Professor registered a trademark, Rentokil. The company was called Disinfectants & General Products, Limited, of 71 Newington Causeway, London SE1; Disinfectant Manufacturers, and the date was the 29th of September 1924.

He had originally intended to call the product Entokill, being a portmanteau word comprising the Greek work for insect, *entomon*, with the English word *kill* added on. For some reason, the Board of Trade disliked this word and obliged him to put a consonant in front of it. Quite why he chose R is not recorded although, faced with such impossibilities as Bentokill, Dentokill and Mentokill, for instance, his choice was not a large one. Rentokil has a pleasant sound and Rentacrowd and Rentacar, Rentavilla, Rentaflower, were forty years away in the future.

It appears that he did this without informing his wife.

> My mother was everything a wife should be to her husband. He did not always understand her true worth. Had he, for instance, taken her into his confidence over the *Rentokil* affair, she would very quickly have got it properly organised. She was an extremely competent and business-like person. Father was just the opposite. Why, then, did he try to go ahead so disastrously with *Rentokil* without taking her into his confidence – better still, into full partnership?

This is a question which can never be answered. It appears that he started the company with one assistant, Miss Bessie Eades, and it is noticeable that from this time he was even shorter of money than before, presumably because he had her wages to pay and the raw materials to buy.

> When I returned from school for the Christmas holidays in 1924 we had left Sherlies and moved to a flat in St George's Square, Pimlico. Somewhere near the Tate Gallery. Our stay there was short-lived and early in 1925 we moved to a rented house in Chislehurst. I do not recall ever having been told the reasons for these abrupt series of moves. In those days children were regarded as adornments, to be seen and not heard; they did not count in the deliberations of adults. And some time during the year we moved again, this time to our final destination, 46 Stanhope Gardens, South Kensington, a small residential hotel.

In February of the following year the *Bioscope* reviewed two more of the Professor's films, both made in 1924.

> *The Swallow-Tail Butterfly* traces the life history of this beautiful creature throughout its transitional stages as caterpillar and chrysalis. Particularly good are the close-ups showing the caterpillar changing and consuming its skin, and subsequently lashing itself to a twig in preparation for its long winter sleep in chrysalis form.
>
> *The Vapourer Moth* deals with the heart affairs of Mothland where, as in the spider world, the wages of love is death.

On the 31st of March, *The Times* carried an article by the Professor on the subject of the Boll Weevil, 'Methods of Control'.

It was L.O. Howard, Chief of the United States Bureau of Entomology, who declared that the boll weevil possesses the unique distinction of having risen from comparative obscurity to be one of the world's chief pests in the space of twenty years.

The eggs which have been laid in the bolls hatch out in about three days, and the grub feeds, as already described, for a period varying from seven to twelve days, when it turns into a pupa, remaining thus for another three to five days. All these stages take place actually inside the boll. The adult beetle which emerges from the pupa is a greyish or brownish insect about a quarter of an inch long.

The triumphant march of the boll weevil across America may be likened to that of the Colorado Beetle, which extended eastward from Mexico in a similar manner until it reached the docks on the Atlantic coast, where numbers literally overflowed into ships which were lying in the harbour. Thus, by pure chance, the beetle was brought to Europe. It is an interesting point to conjecture whether the boll weevil may not likewise be carried across the ocean to bring destruction to other cotton-growing areas beyond the United States.

From the *Morning Post* of the same date we learn that the College of Pestology had held another luncheon. Sir William Simpson, the vice-president, took the chair and Sir Ronald Ross, who had discovered the role played by the mosquito, presented the medal for the best essay on the prevention of malaria to a Mr Shute. According to Lieutenant Moore, now transformed into Mr A. Moore Hogarth by deed poll, there had been between three hundred and four hundred entries. Clearly the College was still having great difficulty in establishing itself and Sir Ronald Ross, in particular, regretted that the Ministry of Health did not seem interested in eliminating the common fly. The headline on this article is 'The Fly Danger'.

Another part of the same paper carried this report:

Poison for Flies

Professor Nearly Loses His Life While Experimenting.

While experimenting in his laboratory with a deadly poisonous gas, known as Lewisite, Professor H.M. Lefroy, of the Imperial College of Science and Technology, South Kensington, nearly lost his life.

On the following Thursday, the *Morning Post* carried an article by the Professor on the Death Watch Beetle, referring to his recent accident in an introduction.

This is not the place for a list of buildings known to be attacked. One wonders if there are any fine buildings unattacked. One sees St. Paul's or Kings College Chapel, glorious stone memorials of the skill of our ancestors, and one forgets that behind the stone is the intricate oak construction that makes possible the stability of the less resilient stone. In all parts of the country ... the story is the same. One hesitates to look into any church, for fear of what one is almost certain to find. One sympathises with the parish authorities who would like to let things be and leave it to a later generation. And really the only reason for trying to awake interest in this question is that treatment has become so much simpler, that the attack may be arrested. This generation may now, by small effort, hand on to the next generation, irreplaceable buildings that will otherwise certainly collapse.

The Society of Antiquaries issued a pamphlet, mentioning that in one church the flying beetles were so numerous that they 'became a nuisance to worshippers'. After his death, it was found that the Professor had given free advice to more than a hundred churches and cathedrals. By the 13th of April, the Professor was well enough to write once more to *The Times*.

Damage to Old Oak.

It is my experience in some scores of cases that the use of turpentine and linseed oil to prevent damage by beetles is quite useless. Had it not been a general practice in the past times we should not have had to deal with many buildings now. Chemistry as applied to entomology is a very recent branch of science and the architect a century ago had only available the few familiar substances out of which he chose, quite empirically, linseed oil and turpentine. Had he used paraffin it would have saved many buildings; he did not have the wide range of chemicals now available.

In August the family went to Belgium.

We spent our last holiday together, a few days in Ostend and then to the seaside resort of Knocke le Zoute, which in those days was virtually an English colony. We stayed in the Globe Hotel and Father soon established himself as a powerful magnet for children from far and wide who flocked round him whenever he came down to the beach and eagerly joined him in digging for worms in the sand or examining the breakwater rocks. He seemed thoroughly relaxed. It was my first trip abroad and I was arrayed in my first dinner jacket.

In letters to the Professor's son, two of these children recalled, in 1980:

The parents were left playing whilst your Father had all the young collecting sand flies or sea bugs, beetles, insects etc. off the upright wooden breakwaters. It was fun & messy & smelly – all of which appealed to the young and your Father's enthusiasm spurred us on. The jars appeared mysteriously (from his pockets?!!). Your Mother was not so enthusiastic when the half-filled jars were on her dressing table. These she put on the outside window-sill – only to be told, later, that they had fallen through the glass-domed roof into the kitchen. No one had any ill effects!!

I've been in touch [with my sister] about the episode of the grubs in the jars on your parents' bedroom window sill at Le Zoute. It overlooked the glass-roofed kitchen area and when the wind blew rather strongly one day they blew off & all landed up on the kitchen table, much to the consternation of the kitchen staff – and of course a repair followed fairly abruptly – ! I can remember this being related, also your Mother saying what ghastly smells she had to endure from various 'brews' of unknown contents which your Father frequently experimented with at home, also from lost or forgotten specimens. Of course we *loved* following your Father along the shore & digging up grubs various at the water's edge – He must have looked like the Pied Piper with all the children gathering round.

Then, in October, at the beginning of the academic year, the Professor returned to Imperial College, while his son went up to Trinity College, Cambridge. He left shortly before the beginning of full term, with his mother, who stayed for a few days with a Lefroy cousin.

My farewell with Father was brief in the extreme. A quick 'good luck' and a handshake and he hurried off to his office and lab in Exhibition Road to plan the experiment that was to lead to his death a few days later. No word of advice about the perils, female and otherwise, that I might find in a great University after leading a wholly sheltered girl-free life until then. His mind was totally absorbed in fulfilling his perceived destiny.

CHAPTER **XXIII**

Somewhere between the laboratory, in Exhibition Road, and St George's Hospital, at Hyde Park Corner, the Professor's wallet and his papers disappeared. The hospital put out an urgent SOS for their return, over the radio, but they were never recovered. He lay, completely unconscious, for four days before dying.

A post mortem was conducted at the hospital on the 15th of October, shortly after midday. The report on this mentions that the lungs were 'congested and somewhat oedematous' and that the heart was 'somewhat enlarged and very flabby'. There were 'signs of congestion' in the liver, the pancreas and the stomach and the colon is noted as having been 'enormously distended'. The actual cause of death was 'chronic atrophy of cortex of cerebrum; fatty degeneration of the myocardium', the muscular part of the heart. The time of death is given as 6.25 p.m. on the 14th of October 1925.

On the 16th, the Westminster Coroner, Mr Ingleby Oddie, held an inquest and this was reported in some detail in *The Times* on the following day:

Mr. Langlois Lefroy identified the body as that of his cousin, who was Professor of Entomology at the Imperial College of Science and Technology, South Kensington.

Mr. Francis Maclean Scott, of Stanhope Gardens, where Professor Lefroy lived, said that on Saturday, about 1.10 p.m., he saw Professor Lefroy and noticed that he was staggering. The witness questioned him about this and he said: 'Yes, I have had too much vapour.' Professor Lefroy had told him that he was experimenting on the larvae of house flies. He was trying to destroy them with a vapour which he called wood oil. The witness took Professor Lefroy to his room and took his boots, collar and tie off. The Professor could not stand up. He was very giddy, but his speech and senses were all right. Professor Lefroy was asleep till about quarter to 4. He was breathing regularly and seemed perfectly all right. When he woke up the Professor began to tell the witness what he had been doing.

The CORONER. – What did he say?

The Witness. – He said, 'The little beggars have got the best of me this time.'

Professor Lefroy, the witness continued, said he would have to go back to the College, as he wanted to lock up the larvae. At half past 5 he seemed perfectly all right and was reading a novel. The witness offered to go back to the College with him, and Professor Lefroy invited him to bring his *fiancée*, who was interested in the Professor's work. They all went round to the College. The Professor kept them amused, showing them over the building. He seemed perfectly all right and climbed up a steep ladder to the fly farm on the roof. He took them into the poison chamber, and showed them his vaporizing mechanism. He turned it on, and a cloud of practically invisible vapour rose and filled the room. He did not, however, put in the wood oil because he felt it would smell so badly. Before he left the poison chamber, he opened the window very wide. He also pointed to a bottle on a shelf and said, 'I am not going to touch that, because if it fell none of us would survive for a second.' They left the College at 6.30, the Professor coming down and seeing them off. He said that he had some letters to write, and the witness assumed that he would follow them to the hotel shortly.

George Charles Sturton, doorkeeper at the College, said that he had a key of Professor Lefroy's laboratory. About 7 o'clock on Saturday evening he went to the Professor's rooms. He heard no sound or movement and there were no lights. He went through the whole building and about 8 o'clock Mrs Lefroy called and asked if he had seen the Professor, as she was feeling rather anxious about him. They went up to Professor Lefroy's rooms. They turned on the light and could find no trace of him there. They then tried the laboratory door, which was locked, knocked on it and called out the Professor's name. They heard a gurgling noise inside, as if someone were breathing heavily. Mrs. Lefroy said, 'He is in here. Open the door quickly.' The witness found that the door was locked, but he had the key of another door leading from the laboratory into a passage, and he immediately went and opened the door. The laboratory was in darkness, and with the aid of a lamp the witness saw the Professor lying inside, face downwards on the floor. He dragged him out and noticed that there was a strange smell in the room. The Professor was unconscious at the time.

Dr. Scott Edwards, house physician at St. George's Hospital, said that when he saw Professor Lefroy he was absolutely unconscious. He was blue and was breathing quite heavily, and throwing up from his throat a reddish froth, which was pouring out in huge quantities. The witness described the methods adopted in the attempt to save the Professor's life. He died at 5.25 p.m. on October 13. The witness gave evidence as to the *post mortem* examination and was questioned by the Coroner as to the conditions of the organs. He said that there was no sign of any malignant disease. The Professor was a victim of very chronic toxaemia which had been carrying on for a period of six or seven years.

In reply to further questions, the witness said that the Professor would have required a second dose of poison to produce the condition he found. He was sure he had had a second attack, which caused the red froth. The witness was of the opinion that Professor Lefroy died from cardiac failure brought on by oedema and congestion of the lungs. His state of coma was due to the sudden inhalation of another poison on top of chronic toxaemia due to the inhalation of some poisonous gases.

Miss Olive Lodge, who assisted Professor Lefroy in his research work, said she could not even suggest the nature of the poison gas which Professor Lefroy had been using.

The CORONER, in summing up, said that Professor Lefroy had met with previous adventures in the course of his experiments. He was poisoned in March last, and poisoned earlier in the same day on which he apparently took a fatal dose. He worked very much alone and did not disclose the nature of the substances with which he was experimenting. That was why the evidence as to what brought about his death was so vague and nebulous. The only clue was in the medical evidence, which was that he was suffering from a chronic toxaemia – a form of blood poisoning – extending over a number of years, and probably due to repeated inhalation of poisonous vapours. On top of that chronic condition he had another dose at midday on Saturday, and finally a fatal dose on the evening of the same day. He was experimenting with poisonous gas in his endeavour to find a cure for certain insect plagues. He was doing great work. Professor Lefroy was a brilliant research worker who had lost his life in trying to benefit the human race.

The CORONER returned a verdict of 'Death through Misadventure'.

The obituaries and tributes flooded in. Alone among them, the *Morning Post* carried this information, under the heading 'Heroic Sufferer from Cancer'.

Only a few of his intimate friends knew that he was suffering from inoperable cancer.

A *Morning Post* correspondent, who interviewed Professor Lefroy about six months ago, writes: 'He was at that moment particularly enthusiastic about the destruction of the death-watch beetle, and, despite great stress of work, agreed to write an account of how the evil should be fought.'

'I must get it off,' he said, 'within the next ten days, because I am to go into a nursing home to be "fattened up" for an operation.'

Certain delays occurred which necessitated the revisiting of the Professor at his laboratory. He had left the nursing home because the surgeons after studying his condition had decided that an operation would be useless. He continued his work at the laboratory, knowing that he might drop dead at any time and that his limit of life was three years.

The fact that Professor Lefroy knew that he was working under sentence of death only stimulated his activities.

It seems almost impossible that this information could have been concealed from his wife, but it is quite certain that it was concealed from his son.

Nowhere is the possibility of suicide mentioned, and it is in fact impossible that a man of such integrity and intelligence could even have contemplated such a thing. It may, however, have crossed the minds of the brother who would not let him be buried at Crondall and of the widow who would never visit his grave. During their stay at Knocke le Zoute, she had obtained a promise from him not to make any further experiments involving poisonous gases.

She was left with his life insurance policy which yielded an income of about £3 a week, which she found would go further in France. She moved to Dinard, in Brittany. A Kitchener Scholarship, established for the sons of needy Army officers, was obtained for their son, largely through the good offices of General Caddell, on the grounds of the Professor's active service in Mesopotamia in 1916.

With some help from a cousin, Langlois Lefroy, he was able to complete the Honours course at Cambridge in 1928. He immediately joined the Burmah Oil company, then a quiet little company producing oil in Burma, and by the end of that year was actually in that country, not returning for his first leave until 1933.

The College of Pestology instantly tried to create a Lefroy Laboratory of Applied Biology and started to appoint a committee. In a surprising reference to the Professor's 'last wishes', they withdrew their Gold Medal for 1926, organising instead an international competition for an essay not exceeding a thousand words on 'the bed bug menace and its solutions'. This was to be called the Maxwell-Lefroy Gold Medal Essay. The letter from Mr A. Moore Hogarth containing this information is dated the 17th of October 1925, and it was published in the *Daily Telegraph* on the 19th. The College was to go through one more metamorphosis as the Institute of Micro-Biology before sliding quietly into oblivion in the middle of the 1930s.

None of the patents applied for by the Professor himself seems to have succeeded commercially. His last application, with Bessie Eades, was made in 1925, from Dacre Street, London SW1. Miss Eades, it now appears, was the business manager at Rentokil Limited. The laboratory assistant was a relation of hers, John McConnell, later to join her on the Board.

In 1928, while Professor Lefroy's widow was still in Dinard and his son was moving from Cambridge to Rangoon, Miss Eades re-registered the company as Rentokil (Sales) Limited. According to herself, she had bought the rights of the timber fluid formulations from the Professor's widow. There is no written record of this purchase, either in the archives of the Lefroys or of the present Rentokil Company. A sum of £90 is mentioned. It seems most unlikely that the Professor's widow, or still more, his son, would have parted with anything of such importance for so little. Their suspicions would have been immediately aroused.

The company then formed, however, continued trading without any further reference to the family. In their first full year of trading, 1929/30, they made a net profit of £256.6s.3d. In March 1932 a claim was made against the new company on behalf of the executors of the Professor for certain royalties alleged to be due, 'the company being advised that by reason of the assignment to the company of the formulae the company is liable for a large portion of such claim, solicitors arranged settlement.'

A sum of £21 was paid out.

In January 1934, the Agricultural Research Centre at Pusa was completely destroyed, buildings, laboratories and records, by one of the worst earthquakes ever to strike that region. It was never rebuilt.

In 1943, the Insect House at the London Zoo was destroyed by a German bomb, with all its records.

The Lefroys spent the years of the Second World War in India, in Assam and Chittagong, returning by flying boat in 1946. Cecil Maxwell-Lefroy went on to become General Manager of the Burmah Oil Company from 1954 to 1959, when he retired with a CBE. He was responsible for easing Burmah Oil out of Burma and has since written two books, *The Peoples of Burma* and *The Peoples of Ceylon*.

By the end of the war, in 1944, Rentokil (Sales) Limited, operating from 168 Stockwell Road, SW9, having been bombed out of their previous premises at 171 Bermondsey Street, SE1, were able to declare an annual profit of £18,000. They went from strength to strength, merging with the British Ratin Company in 1957.

Rentokil, the name of the actual fluid, was by this time a household word, and in 1960 the entire group was re-named Rentokil Group Limited, under which name it trades to this day.

*   *   *

The work of a pioneer is never lost. In the scientific world, research work cannot be undone. It may be disputed; it may be discarded; it may be discredited; but it is there, either pointing a way ahead or indicating the entrance to a cul-de-sac.

Westminster Hall still stands, with its ancient timbers in the roof, as do countless other irreplaceable buildings treated with the original fluid in the Twenties and Thirties. The principles on which it was formulated still hold good today.

Harold Maxwell-Lefroy's wars against houseflies and lice, conducted with as much publicity as possible, made the British public aware of them as menaces; his wireless broadcasts, the films he helped to make, brought insects, hitherto regarded as of some insignificance, into the public eye, both as friends and enemies.

The sugar industry still flourishes in Barbados, rising from its lowest point in 1899. There is a large silk industry in India, gradually given new life after 1917.

There is still a Chair of Entomology at Imperial College. The Imperial Bureau of Entomology and the Annals of Applied Biology, under other names and in other hands, still exist.

The population of India has more than doubled since Harold Maxwell-Lefroy first went there. Some of their crops may be new but the insects that prey on them are the ones he described. To this day, anyone involved in crop protection will consult *Indian Insect Pests*, many of which are still controlled in the old-fashioned way, re-designated 'ecological'. If his prophesies about the spread of insect pests by air have not come entirely true, that may well be because he made them.

His pupils, and their pupils, went all over the world, improving the lot of humanity wherever they could and leaving behind a body of work which remained after the Empire which had supported them had ceased to exist.

But, best of all perhaps, in 1984, *Indian Insect Life* went into its fourth Indian edition.

INDEX